PHANEROZOIC HISTORY

PERIOD	DURATION (MYR)	SIGNIFIC...		

P H A N E R O Z O I C E O N

QUARTERNARY	1.6	 Rise of human beings	ICE AGE
TERTIARY	64.8	Radiations of fishes, mammals and flowering plants	
CRETACEOUS	77.6	First flowering plants. Radiation of bony fish last dinosaurs	EXTINCTION
JURASSIC	64	First birds widespread dinosaurs first flying reptiles	
TRIASSIC	37	First dinosaurs first mammals	MARINE EXTINCTION
PERMIAN	41	Widespread reptiles first mammal-like reptiles	MASS EXTINCTION
CARBONIFEROUS	74	Coal-forming forests widespread amphibians first reptiles first coniferlike plants	ICE AGE
DEVONIAN	48	Vertebrates invade land radiation of vascular land plants	EXTENSIVE MARINE EXTINCTION
SILURIAN	30	Plants invade land first "fish" with jaws	
ORDOVICIAN	67	First nautiloid molluscs and jawless "fishes"	EXTINCTION & ICE AGE
CAMBRIAN	65	Continued evolutionary radiations Early animals with hard parts	

| VENDIAN INTERVAL | 100 + | Rapid evolution of many different soft-bodied multicellular animals |

NASA SP-478

THE EVOLUTION OF COMPLEX AND HIGHER ORGANISMS

WITH A FOREWORD
BY
PHILIP MORRISON

A Report prepared by the participants of Workshops held at
NASA Ames Research Center, Moffett Field, California
July 1981, January 1982, and May 1982

Edited by

David Milne, David Raup, John Billingham,
Karl Niklaus, and Kevin Padian

Prepared at Ames Research Center

Scientific and Technical Information Branch   1985
National Aeronautics and Space Administration
Washington, DC

Library of Congress Cataloging in Publication Data
Main entry under title:

The Evolution of complex and higher organisms.

(NASA SP   ; 478)
Summary of proceedings of the ECHO Science Workshops
held in July 1981 and in January and May 1982.
Bibliography: p. 177
1. Evolution—Congresses. 2. Life on other planets—
Congresses. I. Milne, David. II. Ames Research Center.
III. ECHO Science Workshops. IV. Series.
QH359.E933 1985   575   85-7159

TABLE OF CONTENTS

CHAPTERS

BRIEF TITLES AND CREDITS FOR COVER AND CHAPTER FRONTISPIECES

FOREWORD

Granite outcrops all but proclaim their endurance; nothing is proverbially older than the hills. There is some truth in the observation. Here and there, geologists have found some very old rocks indeed. But endurance in fabric turns out, as we all know, to be deceptive. No understanding is so striking as the recent demonstration by geologists that the wide Atlantic is a transient piece of geography; only a couple of hundred million years ago it resembled the narrow Sea of Cortez. The Andes and the Himalayas are more juvenile still; there must have been Everests in the past, maybe twice as high as our present mountain, that wore down to mere rolling plateaus.

No, the way to last a long time is humbler, if more complex: survive not in fabric, but in form. All manuscripts are fragile, but inducing many loyal readers to demand copies preserved Plato's works more than all the rest. Quite a few modest microorganisms of the soil preserve a form that has a pedigree a couple of billion years long. Their ancestors were fleeting, but they had the knack of self-reproduction.

Biochemistry and its prodigious offspring, molecular biology, have placed on the agenda of science the search for the origin of living self-reproduction. We know that the discovery of that powerful means to persistence belongs on Earth to very ancient times. The thread of life has spun out here for at least three and a half billion years, generation after generation of adequate copies.

For the first four-fifths of that time, all life was lowly. Only the dreamers hoped for some Mars desert rat to pose in front of the Viking facsimile camera; the investigators instead prepared a chemical search for microorganisms. That was the plain message from Earth experience. Life was not scarce on our Earth during its first two billion years or so; it was copious. But it was small. Today our main iron ore deposits are very plausibly the remains of microbial activity in that long past; they stretch at present unbroken across whole provinces. Yet chemistry, not cameras, would have been required to detect that vast veneer of life.

Nor was that early life simple, rudimentary, stereotyped. On the contrary, it was at least as biochemically varied as are the life forms we encounter every day — say ourselves or our domesticated plants and animals. The old forms, like their counterparts of today, found sulphur and iron quite workable as elements of their nutrient systems; as for our indispensible oxygen, many could take it or leave it alone. Molecular engineering was already well developed, the key intricate adaptors and cassettes of the genetic mechanisms at hand more than a billion years ago.

But that intricate world of early life was a shallow world. Life was a surface coating, never far from water, never high, dry, deep. It was a world of chemical effects, a kind of generalized biotic rust on the water edges, decisive perhaps for determining the very composition of the atmosphere and sea, but still, silent, bland. It was a world of damp rocky crusts and mud flats. It was intensely alive, less perhaps to eye and ear than to inquiring nose — had any conscious witness been present.

About eight hundred million years ago, multicellularity was invented and reinvented in many lineages, perhaps a score of times. Cells changed little, but they learned certain indispensible chemical tricks. What they really came to learn was how to live cooperatively. The outcome was the emergence, step by step, of the living world of wing and blossom, fluke and carapace, and green blade, through all the changes that now line the halls of our museums.

Perhaps we can describe the change as life's entry into fully three-dimensional space. The biosphere is still a thin layer in planetary terms, but not on the scale of living organisms. They inhabit the depths and the heights; the oak, like the kelp, holds fast to ground, yet can feel the Sun high above. While the old forms grew in place, even a small animal now knows acres of territory, and the sedentary grasses sow the wind.

x

The other side of the coin of diversity seems to carry a burden of vulnerability. Specialized forms appear and vanish as the circumstances of life change. Here on a planet among planets near a star, the astronomical neighborhood has newly been claimed as a major element in evolution. Comets and asteroids, orbital perturbation, supernovae — even the approach of clouds of galactic dust — are celestial sources of change in the living thread, along with the more evident possible effects of changes within the Sun.

Maybe ours is a safe star, maybe not. Multiple star systems offer other histories to their planets, if any exist. And planets with less drift and tilt might be "safer" still; the argument is attractive that a planet less variable than the Earth — with less ice, less drift — might be altogether *too* safe for a varied evolution.

All these topics are here satisfactorily laid out, an excursion into science between human biology and microbiology that represents a striking novelty for space-oriented readers. Only one question enters the reader's mind that is not addressed here. The time scale of the rise of cellular life is a billion years; that of the important changes in the evolution of the complex forms at least an order of magnitude less; but the rise of human language and of our most important artifacts, such as the telescope, must be counted in millenia and centuries. That time scale implies another distinct chain of evolution, that of culture and intelligence, without the study of which our effort to understand the rise of communicative societies cannot be held complete. Therein lies another story entirely, for another time.

From the Vendian to the Holocene the narrative runs, full of puzzles, happy solutions, twists and turns. We have a great deal of high interest and no less subtlety to learn, but the promise of success is plainly here. The origin of cells as catalysts in the large is a grand question, and one whose study is well deserved. But that chancy, contingent, baroque expansion of cells into complex forms — right up to the evolution of geologists — needs new attention, too.

Our attention now is directed outward, to distant yet powerful forces in the sky. Their subtle promptings and occasional ruder intrusions over ages past have guided and shaken the Earth and its living things. The cells have always known of them and have taken them into account; it is only we humans who have recently realized how compelling those disturbances from space can be.

The authors of this report invite us to consider these age-old, yet new-found factors in the story of terrestrial evolution, and provide us with a chart for exploring those unknown reaches. Thanks to their effort and collective insights, that exploration can now proceed.

Philip Morrison
Massachusetts Institute of Technology

PREFACE

This report was written by scientists from many disciplines who met to consider the broad question of the possible effects of events in space, and of the properties of planets, stars and satellites, on the Evolution of Complex and Higher Organisms (ECHO). The objectives, defined before the first meeting, were as follows:

1. To assess the likelihood that extraterrestrial events had played a role in the development of complex life on Earth throughout the last one billion years

2. To determine whether the study of those events, their geologic signatures, and their effects on life could be of value to NASA

3. To determine whether knowledge of those interrelationships could contribute to a better understanding of the nature and distribution of complex extraterrestrial life

A positive response to these objectives was evident throughout the first meeting. Work turned to the task of outlining the vast potential for richly productive collaborative work that was evident in this new area of inquiry. Geneticist conferred with solar physicist and paleontologist, oceanographer discussed topics of mutual concern with asteroid physicist and zoogeographer, and other exciting intersections of views from different disciplines occurred throughout the Workshop sessions. The insights, discussions, and resolutions generated during the meetings, supported by analysis, writing, and communication during the two intervening periods, and followed by nearly a year of editorial finalization with additional inputs from the participants, culminated in this report.

The completion of the report marks the end of the unusually stimulating exchanges that accompanied its preparation. Studies of the intriguing relationships among the evolution of complex life, events in space, and past and present properties of planet Earth, on the other hand, have barely begun. It is the authors' hope that completion of this volume signals a beginning to the task of exploring those recently recognized relationships, with the ultimate realization of an exciting new potential for human understanding of life, space, and the Earth.

The 2-day meetings, called the ECHO Science Workshops, were held in July 1981 and in January and May 1982. The Workshops were carried out in conjunction with the Extraterrestrial Research Division at the NASA Ames Research Center, with the guidance and support of the Division of Life Sciences at NASA Headquarters in Washington. Dr. David Raup, of the Department of Geophysical Sciences, University of Chicago, served as the Chair of the Workshops. Notes taken at the meeting by Dr. David Milne, of the Evergreen State College, served as the basis for the minutes of these meetings. Dr. John Billingham of the NASA Ames Research Center organized the Workshops.

Special thanks are due to Mary Jeffers, Vera Buescher, and Lorraine Mitvalsky, who were responsible for the excellent organization of the meetings and for secretarial assistance; and to Bruce Lieberman, who recorded the sessions. Also thanks to R. K. Bambach for supplying figure III-5; K. J. Niklas, B. H. Tiffney, and A. Knoll for supplying figures III-8 and III-9; J. J. Sepkoski, Jr. for supplying figures III-10 and III-11; and J. J. Sepkoski, Jr. and A. I. Miller for supplying figure III-4. Without all of these people, it would not have been possible to produce this report.

David H. Milne
March 14, 1983

MEMBERSHIP

SCIENCE WORKSHOPS ON THE
EVOLUTION OF COMPLEX AND HIGHER ORGANISMS

Dr. David Raup, Chair
Department of Geophysical Sciences
University of Chicago, Chicago, Illinois

DR. RICHARD BAMBACH
Department of Geological Sciences
Virginia Polytechnic Institute
Blacksburg, Virginia

DR. W. H. BERGER
Scripps Institute of Oceanography
University of California, San Diego
La Jolla, California

DR. JOHN BILLINGHAM
Ames Research Center
Moffett Field, California

DR. JOHN BRIGGS
Department of Marine Science
University of South Florida
St. Petersburg, Florida

DR. SHERWOOD CHANG
Ames Research Center
Moffett Field, California

DR. W. A. CLEMENS
Department of Paleontology
University of California
Berkeley, California

DR. DAVID DESMARAIS
Ames Research Center
Moffett Field, California

DR. JOHN EDDY
National Center for Atmospheric Research
Boulder, Colorado

DR. ALFRED FISCHER
Department of Geological and Geophysical Sciences
Princeton University
Princeton, New Jersey

DR. ROBERT GARRELS
Department of Marine Science
University of South Florida
St. Petersburg, Florida

DR. JACK KING
Department of Biology
University of California
Santa Barbara, California

DR. ROGER MILKMAN
Department of Zoology
University of Iowa
Iowa City, Iowa

DR. DAVID MILNE
The Evergreen State College
Olympia, Washington

DR. KARL NIKLAS
Section of Plant Biology
Cornell University
Ithaca, New York

DR. KEVIN PADIAN
Department of Paleontology
University of California
Berkeley, California

DR. JAMES POLLACK
Ames Research Center
Moffett Field, California

DR. PETER H. RAVEN
Missouri Botanical Garden
St. Louis, Missouri

DR. RAY REYNOLDS
Ames Research Center
Moffett Field, California

DR. DALE A. RUSSELL
Paleobiology Division
National Museum of Natural Sciences
Ottawa, Canada

DR. J. JOHN SEPKOSKI, JR.
Department of Geophysical Sciences
University of Chicago
Chicago, Illinois

DR. EUGENE SHOEMAKER
U.S. Geological Survey
Flagstaff, Arizona

DR. BRIAN TOON
Ames Research Center
Moffett Field, California

DR. JAMES VALENTINE
Department of Geological Science
University of California
Santa Barbara, California

POSTSCRIPT

The success of the ECHO meetings has been underscored by dramatic research developments that took place after the report was written. Largely as a result of interactions at the meetings, two of the participants (Raup and Sepkoski) launched a statistical analysis of data bearing on a proposition made earlier by another of the participants (Fischer) to the effect that biologic extinctions on Earth have had a periodic distribution in geologic time and that the periodicity is driven by extraterrestrial forces. The publication of this new analysis in 1984 led, in turn, to the publication of no fewer than five papers by geologists and astrophysicists proposing mechanisms for the extraterrestrial driving force. Prominent is the suggestion that the Sun has a companion star which, at perihelion, causes increased bombardment of the Earth by Oort Cloud comets. Whereas this line of research is far from complete, it is clear that the ECHO meetings played an important role in catalyzing these new initiatives in space research, initiatives which may have far-reaching consequences for biology as well as for the space sciences.

David M. Raup
May 1, 1984

CHAPTER I

INTRODUCTION AND SUMMARY

J. Billingham

A. PLANETARY AND GLOBAL BIOLOGY — A NEW PERSPECTIVE

For many years the Life Sciences Program of the National Aeronautics and Space Administration (NASA) has included studies of the origin and evolution of life. These studies have focused on chemical evolution, the origin of life, the early evolution of life, and the search for life and life-related molecules in the solar system. Inevitably the studies are closely linked with the physics and chemistry of planetary environments — that is, with planetary science.

It has recently become apparent that the existing NASA programs in planetary biology have not addressed some important questions. Previous research work focused upon the biological evolution of microorganisms over most of Precambrian time, but did not consider evolutionary processes operative after the appearance of eukaryotic cells. In other words, the biological evolution of the most recent one billion years, including that of the entire Phanerozoic eon (from 570 myr ago to the present), has not been examined by the NASA planetary biology program. This report is addressed specifically to certain questions about evolution during this latter interval, from that of the first multicellular organisms to that operating today. We have arbitrarily called the eukaryotic and multicellular organisms of this billion-year interval "complex life."

1

It is important to emphasize that what is proposed in this report is the study of complex life in a context that differs from that considered by contemporary evolutionary biologists. Current work in the field, supported by the National Science Foundation (NSF), the National Institutes of Health (NIH) and other organizations, deals specifically with the delineation of the mechanisms of biological evolution on the Earth. These mechanisms are usually intrinsic terrestrial ones, stemming from genetic properties of organisms, their competitive and cooperative relationships, and their relationships with particular terrestrial environments. This report examines the possibility of studying the evolution of complex biological systems in another context, that of space. Specifically, it considers the effects of properties of the universe as a whole upon the evolutionary processes occurring on a planet's surface. What are the effects, on life, of the planet's satellites, of the variability of its Sun, of the meteors and comets that bombard it, of peculiarities of its orbit and rotation, of its passage through the dust clouds and star fields of its galaxy, and of events in the space in which it is situated? Specifically, how have these extraplanetary factors affected life on Earth? No systematic and comprehensive analysis of these potentially important factors has been made, to date. This new view, detailed in the pages that follow, we define as the "ECHO perspective" (ECHO = Evolution of Complex and Higher Organisms).

The ECHO perspective defines several new and important groups of questions that relate evolutionary biology to planetary properties and events in space, and hence to a spectrum of fundamental studies and missions being pursued by NASA.

Questions of a first group address the relationships between biological evolution and events in space. To what extent has the evolution of complex life here on the Earth been affected by phenomena such as Sun-Earth interactions, changes in solar activity, gravitational dynamics of the solar system, astrophysical events such as supernovae, and collisions between the Earth and comets or asteroids? We are now learning that such events can cause periodic changes and irregular disturbances of great significance in the biosphere; their possible influence on biological evolution has only recently been recognized and is poorly understood.

Questions of a second group involve extension of our findings about the evolution of complex life in the familiar terrestrial setting out into the universe as a whole. If we know how life is affected by events in space, then what types of galactic, stellar, and planetary environments, suitable for complex life, can be identified elsewhere in the universe? Are the general principles of biological evolution, as they are understood for the planet Earth, equally applicable to Earth-like planets of other stars? Could the evolution of complex life on planets of other sizes, or situated in different galactic environments, have taken much less time than it did on the Earth? More time? Can complex life exist on the planets of stars in multiple star systems? There are many such questions. At present, they are formidably difficult to answer, but they are clearly important to the biologist interested in extraterrestrial life.

Questions of a third group have to do with the improvements in resolution of past events that can follow from utilizing the geological signatures of extraterrestrial disturbances. An asteroid impact in ancient time might have spread traces of iridium (or some other material) over the entire globe within a year or so. What can we learn of the biogeography, the dispersion of the continents, the climate at various latitudes, and other attributes of the Earth at that ancient time, knowing now that the modern iridium trace identifies sediments that were all forming at the same geologic instant? Can improved understanding of climatic responses to the complex wobbles and movements of the Earth, built into its orbit and rotation at the time of its formation, help us to assign more narrowly constrained age limits to important strata whose times of formation are now estimable only within a few million years? These and other improvements in our understanding of the Earth and its living organisms are likely to follow from recognition and delineation of the various interactions between events on the Earth's surface and properties of space and the solar system.

The members of the Science Workshop Group, who prepared this report, addressed the evolution of complex and higher organisms in a logical sequence of chapters. First, in a chapter entitled Life, Terrestrial Environments, and Events in Space, there is a general statement of our current knowledge of biological evolution, followed by a summary of some of the major categories of research questions that the Science Working Group felt were important. The next three chapters address the terrestrial evolutionary story in some detail. Each of these chapters identifies specific and important research questions that should be included in a program to examine the evolution of complex and higher organisms in the context of space. The next chapter identifies extraterrestrial factors that may have had important effects on the evolution of complex life on the Earth. This chapter also includes specific recommendations for research that is likely to yield new information in this field. Finally there is a brief chapter (Complex Life Elsewhere in Space) that deals with questions about the possible evolution of complex and higher organisms elsewhere in the universe. This chapter identifies problems associated with the study of possibilities for extraterrestrial complex life, as well as feasible research objectives, and proposes, perhaps, the most intriguing (and at the same time the most difficult) research tasks of all.

It is our conclusion that there are many questions of major scientific importance in the ECHO area, and that a research program should be structured by NASA to address these questions. The interdisciplinary nature of the ECHO approach holds promise for the development of new concepts, new hypotheses for testing, and new knowledge of evolutionary biology, now in the context of space. An ECHO program would fill out the scope of NASA work on planetary biology (now confined essentially to Precambrian time), so that it would eventually encompass those crucial events, beginning with the advent of multicellular organisms, that have led to the rich diversity of complex and higher organisms we see today.

We recommend that NASA initiate a modest new study of the evolution of complex and higher organisms in the context of space. The program should be organized along the same structural lines as the existing planetary biology programs, and should heavily involve the scientific community.

We also recommend that NASA's experience in planetary sciences, instrumentation, new technologies, and experiments on orbiting and planetary spacecraft be brought to bear on the functional scientific questions, wherever that is appropriate.

B. SUMMARY OF THIS REPORT

(1) This report examines the subject of the evolution of complex and higher organisms (ECHO) in the context of space.

4

(2) Three major aspects of the link between ECHO and space are considered. The first is the extent to which the evolution of complex life on the Earth has been influenced by events in space (particularly by astrophysical, solar, and solar system phenomena). The second is the important general question of the possibility of the evolution of complex life elsewhere in the universe. The third is the extent to which the geological signatures of extraterrestrial events — whether or not they affected evolution — can be used to refine studies of past geographies, climates, and life.

(3) Following this chapter, there are six chapters (II through VII) that deal with various technical aspects of ECHO. Chapter II provides a detailed synopsis of the report as a whole. The other chapters are arranged in a logical sequence, as follows: background material on the history of complex organisms and terrestrial physical-chemical environments (chapters III and IV); details of evolutionary processes and their responsiveness to environmental and extraterrestrial factors (chapter V); the effects of extraterrestrial phenomena upon evolution (chapter VI); and the potential for complex life elsewhere in space (chapter VII). Each of these chapters concludes with a section on recommended research topics. These research recommendations are summarized at the end of chapter II.

(4) In the past, interactions between scientists of previously isolated disciplines have produced remarkable progress in science. We consider this to be the case with ECHO. The strong stimulus of interdisciplinary thinking was apparent throughout the meetings, and bodes well for the outcome of future research on the evolution of complex and higher organisms in the context of space. More important, the fundamental questions identified by the ECHO Science Working Group are inherently challenging, exciting, and significant. For both these reasons, we conclude that study of the evolution of complex and higher organisms, conducted in the context of space, is a fertile field that holds promise for the development of new concepts, new research endeavors for examination of those concepts, new instrumentation, and a new and broader knowledge of evolutionary biology.

(5) We also conclude that the research areas that have been identified constitute a logical addition to NASA's existing planetary biology program. The incorporation of an ECHO endeavor would complement existing work on the origin and early evolution

of life and would explore the full spectrum of evolutionary events that constitute the subject of planetary biology.

(6) We recommend that NASA undertake a modest new program on the evolution of complex and higher organisms in the context of space. The program should be organized along the same structural lines as those of the existing planetary biology programs, and should heavily involve the scientific community.

(7) We also recommend that NASA's experience with the planetary sciences, instrumentation, new technologies, and experiments on orbiting and planetary spacecraft be brought to bear on the fundamental scientific questions, wherever appropriate.

CHAPTER II

LIFE, TERRESTRIAL ENVIRONMENTS, AND EVENTS IN SPACE

D. M. Raup

A. THE EVOLUTION OF COMPLEX TERRESTRIAL LIFE — AN OVERVIEW

In June 1980 a distinguished research group headed by Luis Alvarez hypothesized that one of the great mass extinctions of the geologic past might have been caused by the impact of a large meteorite. The extinction of the dinosaurs and many other species about 66 myr ago has long been a mystery and, although extraterrestrial causes have been suggested in the past, the Alvarez study revealed the first tangible evidence that such an event might really have occurred.

The work of the Alvarez group has emphasized something that should have been recognized earlier: the Earth is not alone! That is, biological processes on Earth are surely affected (or perturbed) by periodic and nonperiodic events in space. The case for a meteorite impact as the cause of dinosaur (and other) extinctions is not complete; many other biological and physical factors might also have been involved. But even if we find that the dinosaurs died of nonmeteoritic causes, the possible significance of extraterrestrial influences on life remains. Recent studies of cratering records on the Earth, Moon, and planets, coupled with counts of asteroids with Earth-crossing orbits, indicate that large-body impacts must be relatively common over geologic time. Collision rates are high enough that their biological consequences may be important, and should be assessed. And there are many other solar system and astrophysical phenomena that may significantly influence the Earth and its biology. Changes in the Sun's temperature and luminosity, the dynamics of the Earth-Moon system, perturbations of the Earth's orbit, and supernova explosions are but a few of the phenomena that should be investigated from this perspective.

We must begin to determine the extent to which the evolution of complex life on Earth has been influenced by these and other extraterrestrial phenomena. At present, there is a large and significant gap in our knowledge in this area. Thanks in part to NASA efforts, we have learned much about the origin of life on Earth and about the evolution of simple life forms during the first few billion years of Earth history. In general, however, NASA's studies do not encompass the evolution of multicellular organisms, after their appearance about one billion years ago. At the other end of the scale of complexity, we are gradually learning more about the development of intelligence in geologically recent times and about the problem of assessing the likelihood of intelligent life elsewhere in the universe. But what motivated biological evolution on Earth between one billion years ago and the present? Was the development of increasingly complex organisms during this interval inevitable? Could intelligence have evolved much earlier (or later) in the Earth's history? Are extraterrestrial influences important and necessary ingredients? Or did complex life evolve in spite of extraterrestrial influences? These are a few of the questions to be addressed in this report. The general objective is to identify the research that needs to be done to obtain a better understanding of the dynamics of the evolution of higher organisms, with special reference to the effects of phenomena of extraterrestrial origin. An obvious by-product of a research program in this area will be better knowledge of the likelihood of complex (and possibly intelligent) life elsewhere in the universe.

1. The Record of Evolution

Fossils provide the documentation of past life on Earth. The first relatively complete fossil records of higher organisms start in rocks that are about 600 myr old, although sparse fossil evidence of simple multicellularity goes back at least one billion years. The interval from 570 myr ago to the present is generally known as the "Phanerozoic"; rocks from this interval have yielded about 250,000 different fossil species so far. Consequently, there is an enormous data base for the study of the evolution of complex and higher organisms.

There is a popular misconception that the fossil record shows all organisms increasing in complexity throughout all of time. Actually, the fossil record is anything but orderly or straightforward. While it is true that life forms of the present, taken as a whole, show greater average complexity and diversity than do those of late Precambrian time, many groups of fossil organisms do not exhibit a simple, straightforward, general progression toward greater complexity through time. Some organisms living today, such as bacteria and some algae, are among the simplest (at least in form) that have ever lived. Certain organisms of early Phanerozoic time (for example, squid-like forms) were as complex then as their modern relatives are today. Complexity has increased in many lineages over time, by fits and starts in some, more gradually in others. But other lineages have experienced little change (or perhaps even decreases) in anatomical complexity, even as their contemporaries became more complex. It is important to consider the details of this irregular pattern of organic change, as well as the general observation that the average complexity of organisms and communities has increased.

The durations of fossil species are usually short compared to total geologic time. Mean durations or "life spans" of species differ from one biological group to another, but it is rare to find a species that lasted more than 15 myr. Some species appear only for a geologic instant. Because Phanerozoic time spans 570 myr, there have been many turnovers in the biological composition of the Earth. When species or groups of species die out, it is rarely possible to say why. The species that replace the ones that vanish are usually not demonstrably superior. The new species may simply have filled ecological niches or geographic areas vacated by those that have become extinct, or they may have been partially responsible for the extinctions of their predecessors.

In spite of the complexity of the evolutionary record, the broad outlines of ancestor-descendant relationships have been worked out by paleontologists over the past 150 yr. We have also

11

arrived at a reasonably good idea of the time ranges of the principal groups. In other words, the basic evolutionary tree of life has been worked out and it is not likely to change very much as a result of further study. Furthermore, many major aspects of evolutionary processes are fairly well understood. However, our knowledge has many gaps. One such gap concerns the relative importance of recognized modern evolutionary mechanisms in accounting for major evolutionary patterns. In particular, our explanations of the origins and extinctions of many important life forms are less than satisfactory. As noted earlier, only within the last few years has serious consideration been given to possible effects of extraterrestrial phenomena on the evolution of complex life.

2. Dynamics of Evolutionary Processes

At any given time during the Phanerozoic, the Earth was populated by hundreds of thousands (or millions) of species. Each species was part of an evolutionary line of descent, or lineage. It is important to note the distinction between "species" and "lineage," as used here (see fig. II-1). Species are the many separate noninterbreeding populations of organisms that exist at any given time. Each living species is the temporary terminus of a unique evolutionary line of descent, or lineage. The lineage is therefore an ancestor-descendant sequence of populations. Several things can happen to a lineage as it progresses through time. It may remain static, in which case the species that constitutes the lineage remains unchanged for many generations. Or the lineage may be transformed, by natural selection or by other means, after which it is represented by a new species. In the latter case, the original species has not become extinct in the sense of extermination — it has simply been transformed beyond recognition. The term *pseudoextinction* is used for this kind of disappearance of a species. Whether or not the lineage undergoes transformation, there is a statistical inevitability that the lineage itself will eventually die out. This is *extinction*, in the true sense, both of the lineage and of the terminal species. Such extinction causes a decrease in the number of extant lineages (and therefore a decrease in the number of living species), which could lead to the

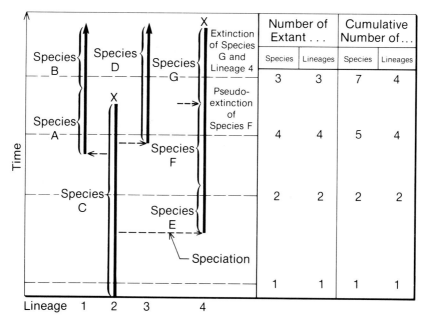

X = Extinction   ↑ = Lineage (and species) still living

Figure II-1.— *Relationship between species and lineages. Each lineage is composed of the most recent living or extinct species and all ancestor species, back to a time of bifurcation. Lineages may be of unequal antiquity.*

disappearance of all life. This has not occurred, however, because of the opposite process: *speciation.* Before a lineage dies out, it may branch to produce one or more new species that constitute the founders of new lineages. This means that a larger taxonomic group of organisms, such as a genus or family, can persist even though some of its species lineages die out. In order for a constant number of living species to be maintained on the Earth, the number of branching (speciation) events must be at least as great as the number of extinction events.

In view of the foregoing, it is clear that evolutionary patterns result from the interactions between the separate processes of extinction and speciation. Within this framework, evolutionary progress toward organisms of higher complexity depends upon both the appearance of new forms and the removal of some existing ones. Extinction makes room for the sorts of anatomical and

13

biochemical innovations that are presumed to arise during speciation events. If extinction were to cease, evolution would probably
come to a virtual halt, because evolutionary change within lineages
is known to be slow and relatively inconsequential. If, on the
other hand, branching of lineages were to cease, extinction events
would eventually eliminate all life.

With speciation and extinction as the driving forces of large-
scale evolution, it is important to identify the environmental factors that favor the two processes.

3. Extinction

Extinction goes on continuously in the natural world. Nearly
all the species that have ever lived are now extinct. Some extinctions were probably caused by purely biological factors having to
do with competition between species for food, living space, and
other resources. But many extinctions, perhaps most of them,
were due to perturbations of the physical environment. Such
events as climatic change (including glaciation); geographic
changes (caused by sea level changes, continental drift, and other
factors); and changes in the composition of oceans and atmosphere undoubtedly played important roles in extinction. If the
Earth and its physical environment were completely stable, it is
probable that many fewer extinction events would take place. As
a consequence, rates of evolutionary change might decrease.

Occasionally during the Phanerozoic, the Earth's biota experienced dramatic increases in extinction frequency: so-called "mass
extinctions" occurred. The mass extinction at the end of the
Cretaceous Period, during which the dinosaurs and many other
organisms disappeared, is an example. The Cretaceous extinction
was only one of about a half dozen mass extinctions, several of
which were even more severe. The extinction that occurred during
the final 10 myr of Permian time, for example, may have eliminated as many as 96% of the species of marine animals then living.
There is considerable evidence that the present destruction of
tropical habitats by man will trigger a new and comparable episode
of mass extinction.

The main effect of mass extinctions has been to reset evolutionary systems in much the same way that a fire or wind-storm

14

may reset an ecological system in a local area. One difference, of course, is that an ecological system can be repopulated by organisms from nearby areas, of species that are identical to the ones that were eliminated. In the case of extinction, however, all new organisms must evolve, from surviving lineages, to replace the ones that became extinct. This resetting, with its accompanying evolutionary replacement of the exterminated species, may be a vital evolutionary process and may be necessary for the development of complex life as we know it. For example, the disappearance of the dinosaurs in the Cretaceous mass extinction may have been an important factor in making possible the subsequent evolution of higher mammals and, eventually, man. Mass extinction may prevent a steady-state condition in evolution, in which plants and animals persist unchanged for very long times.

The foregoing emphasizes the importance of understanding extinction processes, both at the scale of normal "background" extinction and at the scale of mass extinction. As noted above, perturbations in the physical environment are an important cause of extinction. But we are just beginning to investigate seriously the relationship between extraterrestrial phenomena and extinction processes. The extraterrestrial influences may be indirect, acting through such things as climatic change and effects upon plate tectonics. Or, direct effects of extraterrestrial events on plants and animals may occur. The Alvarez study of the possible relationship between meteorite impacts and mass extinction exemplifies the latter category.

4. Speciation

There are many mechanisms that contribute to the formation of new species. Most of these mechanisms involve the isolation of preexisting species into separate noninterbreeding populations. Evolutionary innovations are continually being formed in each isolated population, and each may become a new and distinct species if different and suitable habitats are available. The new habitats that they occupy may originate in many ways. Most arise as a result of constant changes in the Earth's geography and its distribution of environments. If a new island is formed and is colonized by animals or plants from an adjacent island or mainland, the availability of unoccupied habitats on the new island

(and isolation from the main species population) may enhance speciation. On mainland areas, many geological processes, such as the uplift of mountains, are involved in the origin of new habitats that new species may occupy. Thus, the heterogeneity of habitats on the Earth's surface and their constantly changing nature serve to stimulate speciation.

Large-scale evolutionary change is believed to be the result of long-continued and/or repeated speciation events. Because speciation is promoted by environmental instability, long-term evolutionary change is therefore prompted by changes in the physical environment. In turn, environmental instability may be caused or influenced by extraterrestrial phenomena.

5. Physical Environmental Factors

Evolution is heavily dependent upon interactions between organisms and the physical environment. As mentioned, heterogeneity and instability in the environment are very important. Heterogeneity provides the geographic separation of organisms and produces a variety of habitats that foster ecological specializations. Even such simple factors as diurnal light-dark cycles add to the number of ecological opportunities. The more separate habitats and opportunities there are, the more species can be accommodated on the Earth. With more species, the probability of the evolution of specialized and complex organisms is enhanced. Environmental instability is of long-term benefit to the evolutionary process, therefore, because it causes extinction, enhances the need for changing adaptation, and often has the effect of reshuffling the habitats and niches. At some scale, of course, too much heterogeneity and instability could be detrimental to the Earth's biota and its evolution. It is not yet clear how much instability, occurring over what time scale, is optimal for evolutionary processes. This may depend largely upon characteristics of individual species, their histories, and their environments.

Figure II-2 illustrates some of the complex interactions inherent in the evolution of life. Many of these interactions involve features of the lithosphere, many relate to the atmosphere, and many relate to space beyond the atmosphere. Before we can really understand the evolution of complex life on Earth, we must have

16

more information about these interactions and the historical record of their significance for the last 600 myr. In the whole complex, the least explored and least understood features are those involving the direct and indirect influences of events in space on the Earth's biota. How has solar radiation changed over geological time? How have the tides in the Earth's oceans changed as a result of known changes in Earth-Moon distance? How have these changes affected life? Would nearby supernovae be expected to have biological effects and, if so, is there a record of such effects? These are but a few of the extraterrestrial factors to be considered in the body of this report.

6. Complex Life Elsewhere in the Universe

On Earth, life existed in a very simple morphologic state, albeit with high physiological diversity, for about three billion years. Even after higher organisms appeared, it took about 600 myr to develop intelligence as we know it. Need it have taken so long? Most evolutionary biologists would say, "probably not." There is no evidence that intelligence could not have developed in nonmammalian organisms. It may have been only a matter of chance that intelligence developed in the particular lineage that we know led to man. Octopuses and squids, for example, have sophisticated brains. Were their long-extinct relatives, the ammonites, equally sophisticated? What are the real differences, both biological and environmental, between their potential for intelligence and ours? Can this potential be assessed from *a priori* considerations?

It is sometimes claimed that it is impossible to use the Earth's record to estimate the probability that any particular form (such as an intelligent animal) will evolve, because we have only one historical record: that of the Earth. On the other hand, one can argue that we have many partially independent historical records, or "experiments," with which to work. Many separate groups of dramatically different anatomical construction (the major plant and animal phyla) were already established by early Phanerozoic time, and these have maintained their identities ever since. Each of these major groups may be viewed as a separate evolutionary experiment, conducted in partial independence of the others. Patterns of their evolutionary histories are readily comparable. It

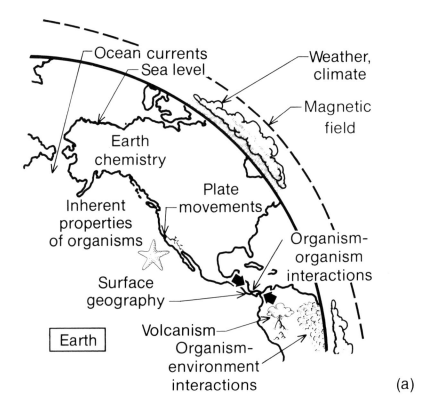

Ocean currents
Sea level
Weather, climate
Magnetic field
Earth chemistry
Inherent properties of organisms
Plate movements
Organism-organism interactions
Surface geography
Earth
Volcanism
Organism-environment interactions

(a)

Figure II-2.— *Factors of importance to the evolution of complex life. (a) Endogenous factors stemming from physical-chemical properties of the Earth, and those of eukaryotic organisms. (b) Factors related to properties of the Sun, and Earth's position with respect to it. (c) Factors originating within the solar system, including properties of Earth as a representative planet. (d) Factors originating in space far from the solar system. Ordinarily, factors b, c, and d have not been considered in studies of the evolution of complex life; their consideration constitutes the "ECHO perspective" and can contribute to a broader understanding of life elsewhere in the universe (d).*

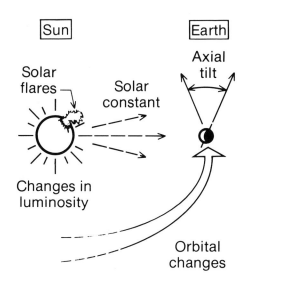

(b)

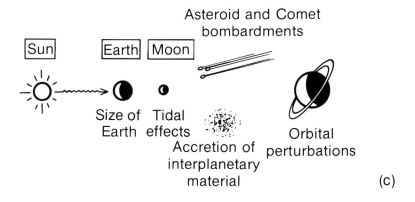

(c)

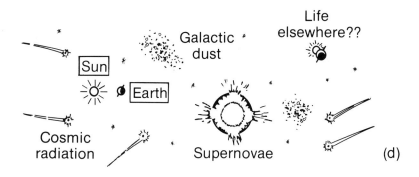

(d)

19

should therefore be possible to make far more sophisticated estimates of the probability that a particular life form will evolve than have been attempted heretofore. For example, powered flight evolved four different times in unrelated organisms (bats, birds, pterosaurs, and insects) and may or may not be evolving today in modern gliding organisms. From these and similar data, it may be possible to recognize the properties and circumstances related to the evolution of flight, and to estimate the probability that flight will evolve in some other Earth-like biosphere. Similar possibilities may exist for estimation of the probability of the evolution of intelligence and other biological constructs in other planetary settings.

It may also be possible to assess quantitatively the importance of environmental perturbations and other physical factors that influence evolution. Would evolution of complex and higher organisms have taken place on the Earth without continental drift? How important are physical factors in causing mass extinctions? Similar questions can be directed toward the environmental regimes of other planets. Models of such systems can only be devised if the effects of physical environmental factors, in the terrestrial and extraterrestrial realms, are properly understood. These interrelationships must be assessed from a wide spectrum of viewpoints. Astronomy, physics, geology, paleontology, and biology will all play equally important roles in this endeavor. For the first time, we have the opportunity to combine diverse fields of knowledge in a study that will help us learn not only about the pattern of life on Earth, but about the possible patterns of life on planets elsewhere in space.

B. SUMMARY OF RESEARCH RECOMMENDATIONS

The Workshop Group identified a number of research areas and specific projects relevant to the general question of the evolution of complex and higher organisms, to the effects of extraterrestrial factors, and to the search for complex life elsewhere in the universe. These recommendations are detailed in the body of the report as separate sections in each chapter. It will suffice here to present an overview of the principal research recommendations compiled by the Workshop Members.

The recommendations fall into three broad categories:

(a) Process and pattern in the evolution of complex life on Earth (chapters III through V)

(b) Analysis of extraterrestrial phenomena as they may affect evolution on Earth or on another planet (chapter VI)

(c) Potential for assessment of properties of complex life elsewhere in the universe (chapter VII)

1. Process and Pattern in Evolution

To understand the influence of extraterrestrial phenomena on evolution, a far better knowledge of the chronology of evolution must be developed. Vast quantities of data are scattered throughout the geologic and paleontologic literature, but at present these data must be collected by hand for statistical (and other) analysis. To improve this situation, *a paleontological data bank and clearing house for the relevant published information is proposed.* With this data bank in place, it will be possible to undertake rigorous statistical analyses of such topics as biologic diversification and mass extinctions as seen in the Phanerozoic record. In particular, analysis of extinction using data from strata containing evidence of large-body impacts is vital in developing a clear understanding of the association in time between such impacts and any evolutionary events.

A lesser but still important research initiative in this context is a proposal to *use NASA's existing capability for image analysis to enhance photographs of some important yet poorly preserved fossils.* The famous Ediacaran fauna of the late Precambrian is an especially appropriate target for image-enhancement techniques. The purpose here is to maximize our understanding of the anatomical complexity of these ancient organisms, including that of their seldom-preserved soft parts, for better delineation of the timing and directionalities of later increases in organic complexity.

To better understand the processes of evolution, several research initiatives have been developed that address basic problems in evolutionary theory. These include *devising better definitions of complexity in biologic systems, analyzing the physical limits of life forms* (basically a problem in engineering and biophysics), *identifying physical and biological factors controlling the rate of evolution, and studying the effects of extreme environmental conditions on an organism's ability to survive and function.* Some of these studies relate directly to existing capabilities for global surveys from satellite data and some relate to ongoing studies of the present and future habitability of the Earth.

One research recommendation may have special relevance. The present-day loss of habitats in the Earth's tropical regions may be the beginning of a major mass extinction of species. By *studying the destruction of tropical forests and the accompanying wave of extinction,* we can learn much about the mechanisms of mass extinctions of the past. This type of study may also provide important answers to questions of environmental planning for the next few decades.

2. Extraterrestrial Phenomena

The Workshop Group identified five major categories of phenomena about which new or expanded information is needed, or in which existing information may be analyzed from a new perspective. These are

    (a) Frequency of large-body impacts now and in the geologic past

    (b) Cyclic and noncyclic changes in the orbit of the Earth having potential for influencing evolution

    (c) Solar variability

    (d) Supernovae and their climatic and biological consequences

    (e) Galactic dust clouds and their possible influence on evolution

The research recommendations specify two broad areas of endeavor: (1) *compilation of the histories of these extraterrestrial phenomena,* as completely as existing data and new field investigations will permit, and (2) *analysis of their direct and indirect effects upon biological evolution.*

Except for knowledge already accumulated on large-body impacts (and on a few other phenomena, such as changes in the Earth-Moon system), the general field of the geologic record of extraterrestrial phenomena is virtually unexplored. Likewise (with the partial exception of supernova effects upon climate), little is known of the effects of these events upon evolution on the Earth.

The greatest imagination and ingenuity will be needed to bring together the necessary theoretical and empirical approaches. Research in these areas will make use of existing information, such as cratering records on the Earth, Moon, and planets, and other data from the full range of NASA programs. Bold and innovative future programs, such as selected explorations of the geology of Mars, can contribute much to our understanding of climatic and other events that are unique to individual planets, and events (such as those caused by stellar variability and supernova effects) that impinge simultaneously on all of the planets in the system. Throughout, the aim will be to document events that have a direct bearing on evolutionary processes as they operate on Earth and, perhaps, on planets elsewhere in space.

3. Complex Life Elsewhere

Questions about the evolution of complex life elsewhere in the universe are easy to pose but difficult to answer. One reason is that we have virtually no data. No life has yet been detected outside the Earth. However, there is now a good theoretical basis for the conjecture that life may be widespread in the universe. As we pose questions about the putative evolution of complex life in the extraterrestrial realm, we are constantly driven back to the fossil record of the Earth, where the data base is large, and to the research questions identified in this report with regard to terrestrial evolution. As these research questions are examined, and as strategies are developed in an effort to reveal solutions, it should be borne in mind that the solutions can be extended to address particular problems of the evolution of complex life elsewhere. For example, if it is found that meteorite or cometary impacts were of evolutionary significance on the Earth, what would be the evolutionary effect of a ten-fold increase in the rate of collision of large objects with some other planet? Of a ten-fold decrease? Which environmental circumstances are necessary, and which are sufficient, for the evolution of complex life? Which circumstances would militate against the emergence of complex life? Are there regions of the galaxy, or of the universe, where life is impossible? Where complex life might evolve much more rapidly than it did on

Earth? What is the probability of the total extermination of complex life, on Earth or elsewhere in the universe, as a result of astrophysical (or endogenous) causes? Research pertaining to terrestrial life, therefore, can produce insight into the evolution and distribution of extraterrestrial life.

Likewise, it is possible to pose testable questions that address extraterrestrial life explicitly. An important task in this area is to *calculate the range of planetary sizes and other properties that would permit an Earthlike orbiting body to support complex life,* if such a planet were situated at a suitable distance from an appropriate star. A second task is to *determine whether the emergence of complex life is inevitable or highly probable, once sophisticated (eukaryotic) cells have evolved.* Third, and of special interest, is the controversial GAIA hypothesis, which proposes that living things have prevented drastic climatic changes on the Earth throughout most of its history. This view, regarded as highly speculative and tentative by many workers, has yet to be rigorously examined. If it proves to be correct, and if climatic stabilization can be shown to be a likely consequence of the activities of life on other worlds as well, then we may expect that extraterrestrial life is abundant throughout the universe. An effort should be made, therefore, to *determine whether the GAIA hypothesis is valid.* And other efforts should be made to determine upper limits of meteor bombardment, cosmic radiation, solar variability, and other phenomena that are permissive of the evolution of complex life, and to identify galactic regions in which nonlethal levels of these factors can be found.

These and other questions are stimulating, and should be asked. We do not recommend devoting a large part of the resources of an ECHO program to addressing them, since they are clearly so difficult to answer at the moment. But we do recommend that attention be paid to them, and that support be given to studies that show promise for making inroads into the problem of understanding the evolution of complex life elsewhere in the universe.

CHAPTER III
GEOLOGIC HISTORY
OF COMPLEX ORGANISMS

R. K. Bambach, J. C. Briggs, W. A. Clemens, K. J. Niklas,
K. Padian, D. M. Raup, P. H. Raven, D. A. Russell,
J. J. Sepkoski, Jr., and J. W. Valentine

A. CURRENT VIEWS OF THE DEVELOPMENT OF COMPLEX LIFE ON EARTH

Complex organisms first arose in the sea, and indeed all lineages of which we have knowledge, living or extinct, originated in marine environments. The record of basic evolutionary patterns that best illustrates the development of organic complexity is therefore that of the marine fossil biota. The trends found in the marine fossil record appear to be paralleled by those seen in the continental record, although the latter occur at lower taxonomic levels.

For Archaean and much of Proterozoic time, the fossil record consists only of remnants of prokaryotic assemblages and of stromatolites, their biogenic structures (fig. III-1). Acritarchs represent the oldest probable records of eukaryotes; these first begin to appear in fossil microbiotas about 1500 million years (myr) ago. Unmistakable eukaryotes (algal macrofossils) are known from about 1300 myr ago (Walter et al., 1976). The first unequivocal animal remains are of Vendian ("Ediacarian") age, appearing perhaps 680 myr ago (Glaessner, 1971; Cowie and Cribb, 1978).

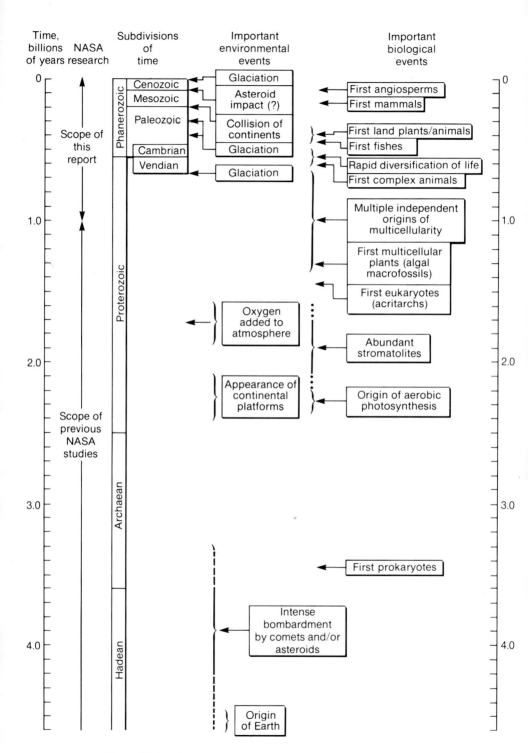

Figure III-1.— *Important events in the evolution of the biosphere.*

There is little in this scattered sampling of those three billion years to indicate whether early evolution was gradual or abrupt. The rise of eukaryotes and of the earliest truly multicellular organisms is poorly recorded, but we can speculate briefly on the significant features of their early evolution.

1. Appearance of Eukaryotes and Multicellularity

Compared with prokaryotes, eukaryotic cells (which comprise all higher plants and animals) are characterized by considerable complexity of parts. A leading hypothesis attributes their origin partly to the amalgamation of symbiotic prokaryotic cells, which eventually became organelles within a host cell (Margulis, 1970, 1981). The host cell was an ingester, which has no known close modern analogs. The organelles gained in this way seem, in turn, to have allowed the cells in which they became components to achieve a higher degree of autoregulation. Eukaryotes are characterized by possession of more complex gene regulatory mechanisms than those of prokaryotes. Complexity of gene regulation lies at the heart of the ability of cells to differentiate, and to form the functionally diverse and distinctive tissues and organs required to produce complex organisms. It is not an unreasonable speculation, therefore, that the evolution of enhanced regulatory ability (which was certainly required to integrate early symbiotic cells into a sophisticated life cycle) underlay the rise of the earliest eukaryotic cells. In turn, improved autoregulatory ability may well have proved to be the key innovation needed to permit evolution of truly complex organisms.

In the last part of the Proterozoic Era, multicellularity appeared independently in many different lineages (Stebbins, in Dobzhansky et al., 1977). This suggests that multicellularity was an easy and adaptively valuable evolutionary innovation, given the kinds of eukaryotic cells and the environmental conditions prevalent at that time. Certainly, multicellularity was essential to the construction of tissue systems and led to the hierarchical structure of metaphyte (multicellular plant) and metazoan (multicellular animal) body plans.

2. Appearance and Radiation of Metazoa

Direct fossil records of the first evolutionary steps in the development of multicellular animals are lacking. It is not clear, therefore, whether their early evolution was gradual or abrupt. Both lower and higher metazoan invertebrate groups first appear as fossils during the late Precambrian Vendian interval, between about 690 and 570 myr ago (figs. III-1 and III-2). If these animals all originated after 680 myr, then the earliest metazoan radiation must certainly be judged as rapid.

Cnidarian and probable cnidarian fossils of Vendian age are relatively common and widespread. They have now been found at many localities on five continents (Glaessner, 1979). Body fossils of wormlike animals (possibly including annelids) and possible protoarthropods and echinoderms are also present; these are rarer and more restricted. The richest associations are known from the work of Glaessner and his colleagues in Australia and of Fedonkin and his colleagues in the western U.S.S.R. Examples of some of these forms are depicted in figure III-3, which illustrates fossils from the Australian Ediacara Hills. Last but not least, various burrows and similar traces are found in rocks of the same age. These include long, sinuous, horizontal burrows and shorter vertical ones, and are almost certainly the work of coelomate metazoans. In sum, the best evidence now available indicates that the first metazoan animals appeared by about 680 myr ago, and that within the next 100 myr they gave rise to a variety of acoelomate pelagic and epifaunal benthic organisms (see also Sepkoski, 1978; Brasier, 1979). Coelomate infaunal forms from this time are known chiefly by their burrows.

Beginning in the late Vendian, about 600 myr ago, and continuing into the Cambrian, an immense evolutionary radiation occurred among marine metazoans (fig. III-2). Within the span of 100 myr, nearly all of the extant phyla whose members have mineralized skeletons appear in the fossil record. In addition, several extinct phyla with skeletons also appear. These include the Archaeocyatha and, perhaps, Hyolitha and various early Cambrian (Tommotian) "problematica" (e.g., the Mitrosagophora, Thambetolepida, Angustiochreida, etc.). In all cases analyzed thus far, the mineralized skeletons functioned as adaptations to life upon (as opposed to within) the sea floor (Valentine, 1973). Most of the

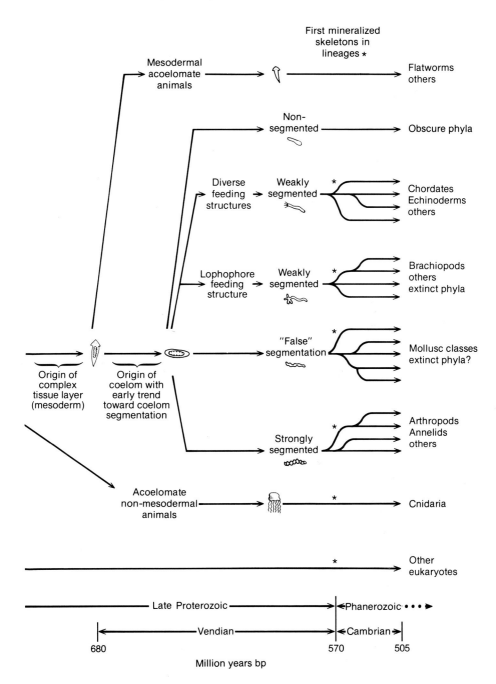

First mineralized
skeletons in
lineages ★

Mesodermal
acoelomate ⟶ ⟶ ⟶ Flatworms
animals   others

Non-
⟶ segmented ⟶ ⟶ Obscure phyla

Diverse   Weakly   ★ ⟶ Chordates
⟶ feeding ⟶ segmented   ⟶ Echinoderms
structures   others

Lophophore   Weakly   ★ ⟶ Brachiopods
⟶ feeding ⟶ segmented   others
structure   extinct phyla

"False"   ★ ⟶ Mollusc classes
⟶ segmentation   extinct phyla?

Strongly   ★ ⟶ Arthropods
⟶ segmented   Annelids
others

⟶ ⟶ Origin of   Origin of
coelom with
Origin of   early trend
complex   toward coelom
tissue layer   segmentation
(mesoderm)

Acoelomate
non-mesodermal ⟶   ★ ⟶ Cnidaria
animals

★ ⟶ Other
eukaryotes

Late Proterozoic ⟶ ◄Phanerozoic • • • ►

◄———————— Vendian ————————► ◄Cambrian➤
680   570   505
Million years bp

Figure III-2.— *A generalized model of the evolutionary radiation of metazoan phyla showing the rapid appearance and divergence of major body plans in the Vendian and early Cambrian periods. (Many short-lived phyla present in the early Phanerozoic eon are not indicated since their relationships are not known.) (After Valentine, "General Patterns of Metazoan Evolution. Patterns of Evolution as Illustrated by the Fossil Record," Elsevier, Amsterdam, 1977.)*

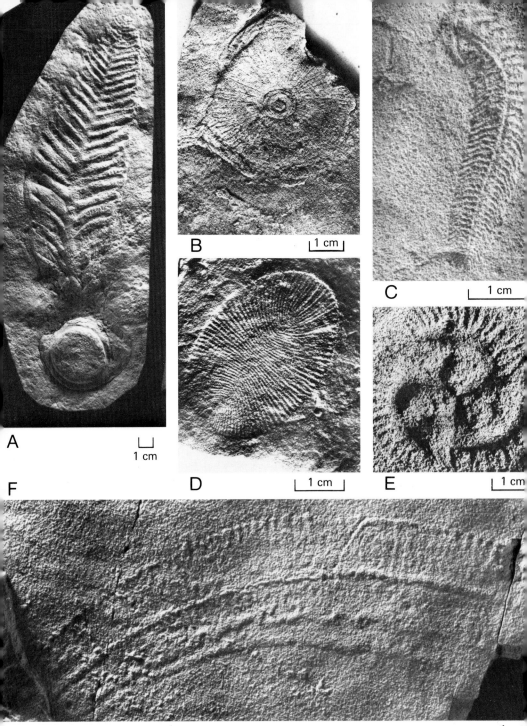

Figure III-3.— *Fossils of Precambrian organisms. A-E from the Ediacara Hills, F from the Brachina formation, Australia. Phyla are as follows: A, B, cnidaria; C, D, annelida; E, uncertain, perhaps of extinct phylum; F, cnidaria. Digital enhancement techniques may clarify certain anatomical details of these ancient organisms. (A, C-F from Cloud and Glaessner, Science, vol. 217, 1982, pp. 783-792, copyright 1982 by The American Association for the Advancement of Science. B courtesy of M. Glaessner.)*

epifaunal coelomate lineages seem to have descended from burrowing ancestors, perhaps with the exception of the Mollusca, which may not be eucoelomates.

In addition to the forms with durable skeletons that constitute the bulk of the fossil record, we are privileged to glimpse the soft-bodied fauna that, at least by mid-Cambrian time, was normally associated with some of the skeletonized communities. This rare opportunity is provided by the remarkably preserved fauna of the Middle Cambrian Burgess Shale of British Columbia (summarized by Conway Morris, 1979a,b). The presence of the annelid phylum is confirmed, priapulids and hemichordates appear for the first time, and chordates are first represented by fairly definitive fossils. In addition, perhaps a dozen lineages are found that are not assignable to any living phyla and which do not represent intermediates or ancestors of living phyla. Instead, they probably represent additional phylum-level body plans evolved during the wave of high-level diversification that characterized the late Precambrian and early Cambrian periods.

Many of the durably skeletonized phyla that have the better fossil records during the Cambrian are represented by a number of major subtaxa (classes or orders; see table III-1). This is true, for example, of the Echinodermata, Mollusca, Arthropoda, and Brachiopoda (see the appropriate chapters in House, 1979). In fact, more than 60% of the animal classes known from the marine fossil record make their first appearances in the Vendian-Cambrian interval (Sepkoski, 1979). Thus, it is clear that the latest Precambrian and early Cambrian periods witnessed the origination and deployment of novel body plans on a scale that was unprecedented and that has not been repeated. The spotty nature of the fossil record and the poor fossilizability of perhaps two-thirds of invertebrate taxa preclude an accurate count of the body plans or a precise estimation of their rates of origin, but one can guess that there were perhaps 50 to 100 phyla and several hundreds of class-level plans involved. (There are only some 31 phyla living today.) The diversification occurred at a time when the number of species was relatively low, so that at times, perhaps each fortieth species (precision here is impossible) founded what is now recognized as a new class or phylum. This early episode of macroevolution was chiefly responsible for the complexity and diversity of modern body architecture in the Metazoa and, with the possible exception

TABLE III-1.— TAXONOMIC CATEGORIES IN BIOLOGICAL CLASSIFICATION AND THEIR IMPORTANCE IN PALEOZOOLOGY

Category or taxon	Paleontologic importance
Phylum	Fundamental division of the animal kingdom, distinguished by unique aspects of the basic "body plans." Arose mostly in the late Precambrian from soft-bodied (presumably small) ancestors; therefore no fossil record of intermediates exists. Evolutionary relationships determined largely from living representatives by embryology and comparative anatomy.
Class	Major division within a phylum, distinguished by basic modifications of the body plan. Most of the marine classes with fossil records appear early in the Phanerozoic. Fossil record contains intermediates between classes in some phyla (e.g., Mollusca).
Order	Higher taxon; new orders appear throughout the Phanerozoic. Marine fossil record shows nearly constant numbers of animal orders from Ordovician to present.
Family	Lowest taxonomic category for which comprehensive, accurate data for all marine and continental animals have been compiled. Data on 5000 or so fossil families show many features in the history of life, such as major evolutionary radiations and mass extinctions. However, many fluctuations in species, such as minor mass extinctions, are not reflected in families.
Genus	Smaller taxonomic unit than the family, therefore showing more detail in evolution. Accurate data have been compiled for only a few groups (e.g., nautiloid cephalopods). Probably between 25,000 and 40,000 fossil genera have been described.
Species	Basic unit of evolution; the "kind" of organism in everyday use. More than 250,000 fossil animal species have been described in the literature over the last 250 years, but no attempt has been made to compile accurate listings of species and their stratigraphic ranges for all phyla. Studies of evolutionary processes in living organisms deal almost exclusively with species (see chapter V).

of the origin of eukaryotic cells, represents the most critical step in the development of the kind of fauna that has led to intelligent life on Earth. Thus, complexity has not accumulated at a steady rate, but has made episodic and geologically rapid advances.

3. Phanerozoic Patterns in the Marine Record

Many important features in the post-Vendian evolution of marine animals can be seen by tracing the diversification of lower taxa, such as families (table III-1) for which accurate data on skeletonized representatives have been compiled (Newell, 1967; Valentine, 1969; Sepkoski, 1979, 1981). The rise in the number of marine families that accompanied the diversification of Cambrian metazoans was extremely rapid and would have resulted in 10^{27} modern families if it had continued until the present. Instead, diversification of Cambrian animals slowed briefly in the middle and late Cambrian period so that the numbers of skeletonized families never exceeded about 130 (fig. III-4). At the beginning of the Ordovician period, another group of animals (which had been present in low numbers since the early Cambrian) began radiating rapidly, resulting in a tripling of the number of marine families in just over 50 myr. This new level of diversity then persisted for the rest of the Paleozoic era (about 200 myr) until the marine fauna was decimated by the late Permian mass extinction. Following that event, a third group of higher taxa radiated, and diversity climbed toward an all-time high in the late Cenozoic era.

The rise in morphological complexity and diversification of the Phanerozoic biotas was associated with changes in the patterns of ecosystem structure. What little is known of ecosystems before the appearance of multicellular organisms suggests that the prokaryotic systems were highly flexible and tolerant of environmental change. Essentially nothing is known of the structure of the early eukaryotic ecosystems. The early multicellular marine animal communities appear to have been relatively simple. Early benthic associations seem to have consisted chiefly of detritivores and low-level suspension feeders (with few obvious predators) that inhabited a relatively restricted range of habitats. For example, the Cambrian fauna occupied only 9 of some 22 different "ecospaces" identified by Bambach (1983). As diversification proceeded, the

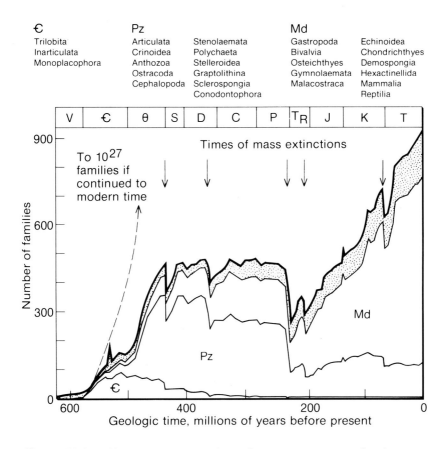

€	Pz		Md	
Trilobita	Articulata	Stenolaemata	Gastropoda	Echinoidea
Inarticulata	Crinoidea	Polychaeta	Bivalvia	Chondrichthyes
Monoplacophora	Anthozoa	Stelleroidea	Osteichthyes	Demospongia
	Ostracoda	Graptolithina	Gymnolaemata	Hexactinellida
	Cephalopoda	Sclerospongia	Malacostraca	Mammalia
		Conodontophora		Reptilia

Figure III-4.— *Changes in the number of marine taxonomic families over geologic time. Upper curve depicts total number of families. Other curves subdivide the total among three major faunas (Cambrian = "C," Paleozoic = "Pz," Modern = "Md") that dominated the seas in succession, and a few other organisms (stippled area). Curves refer mostly to "shelly" forms that leave fossils; about 1900 modern marine families are known, many of which are not shelly. Organisms of faunas C, Pz, and Md are illustrated in figure III-7. Arrows indicate times of the five mass extinctions discussed in the text.*

number of taxa associated with each major ecological zone or guild within communities increased, apparently as a result of processes of speciation among the lineages themselves and by partitioning of the resources of the zones. At the same time, however, new habitats were invaded and new modes of life were taken up. This last point is shown in figure III-5 by the increase in

36

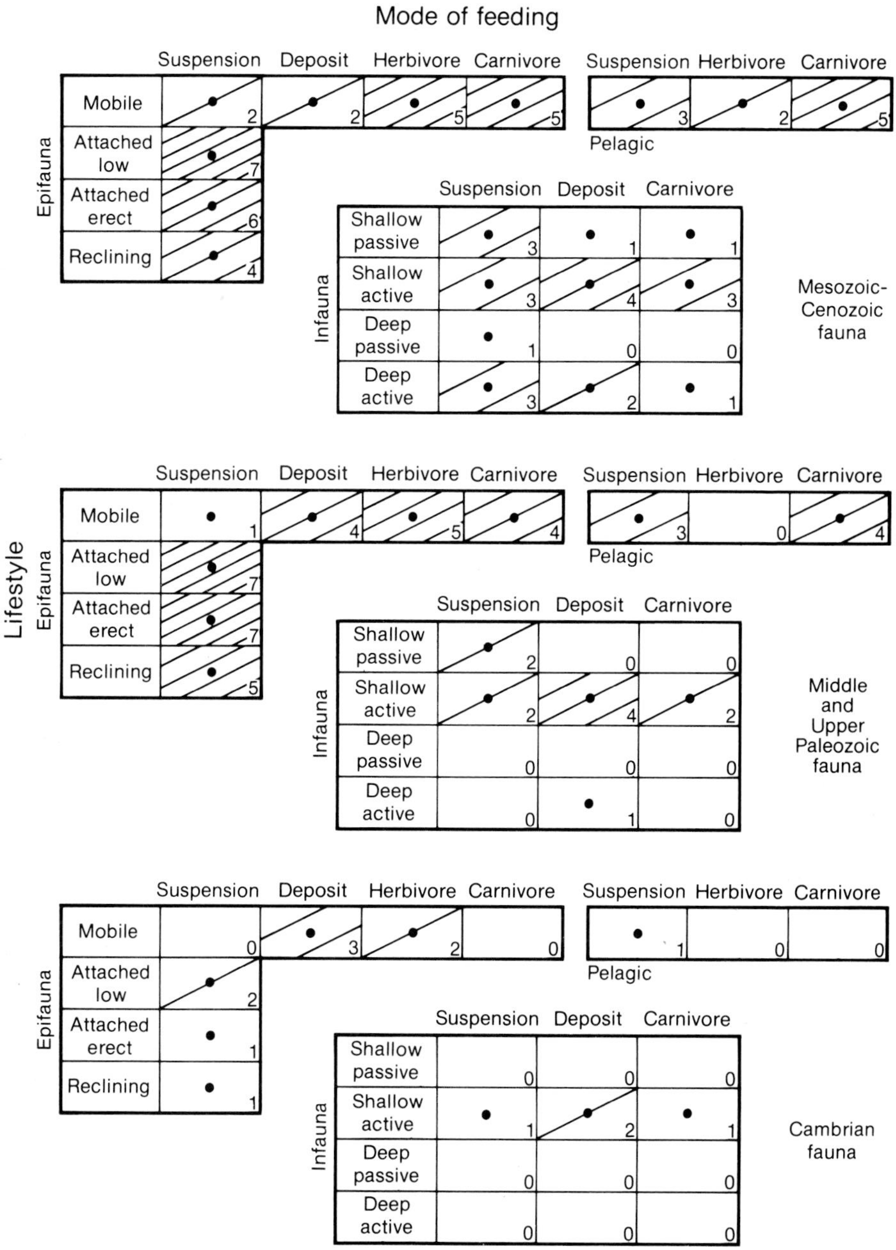

Figure III-5.— *Increase in the complexity of marine communities with time. Each cell represents one possible way of life (labeled on the left) and one mode of feeding (labeled along the top). Numbers and shadings of boxes show the numbers of different groups of animals that practice those lifestyle combinations at the times shown. As time goes by, the number of possible lifestyle combinations actually adopted increases, as do the numbers of groups practicing any particular lifestyle. (Bambach, private communication.)*

the number of occupied cells in the tables for the Cambrian, the later Paleozoic, and finally the Mesozoic-Cenozoic faunas.

Even while some taxa were diversifying and exploiting new ecological zones, other taxa were becoming extinct. Patterns of familial extinction (fig. III-6) indicate that a relatively narrow range of extinction rates ("background extinction") persisted throughout Phanerozoic time (Raup and Sepkoski, 1982). This background extinction was punctuated at irregular intervals by episodes of "mass extinction," the largest of which appear as peaks in figure III-6. The most severe mass extinction of the Phanerozoic was the late Permian event, which eliminated more than half of the marine families and perhaps as many as 96% of

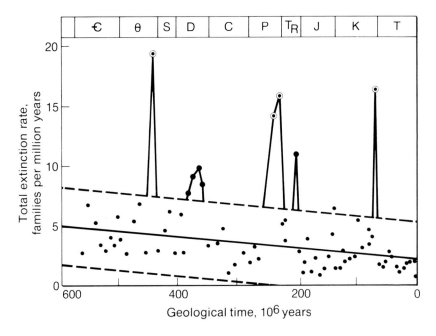

Figure III-6.— *Change in extinction rate of marine families over geologic time. Normal "background" extinction rate is represented by the solid regression line and the dotted 95% confidence band, fitted to the points whose values are less than eight families/myr. The five major extinction episodes appear as spikes above the background band. (After Raup and Sepkoski, Science, vol. 215, 1982, pp. 1501-1503, copyright 1982 by The American Association for the Advancement of Science.)*

the marine species (Raup, 1979). This event decimated the Paleozoic fauna and ushered in the Mesozoic-Cenozoic phase of diversification. Four other episodes of mass extinction, occurring in the late Ordovician, late Devonian, late Triassic, and late Cretaceous periods, had lesser effects on the marine system (although one, the late Cretaceous event, had major effects on land, ending the reign of reptiles and beginning the dominance of mammals). The reasons for the different magnitudes of the mass extinctions and for their variable effectiveness on land and in the oceans deserve close study.

The marine life of the Phanerozoic can be divided into three major faunas or compositional phases (Sepkoski, 1981). The diversities and compositions of these three "evolutionary faunas" are shown collectively in figure III-4 and individually in figure III-7. The first became established in the late Precambrian (Vendian) time and peaked during the Cambrian period. This time was characterized by the establishment of major body plans and subplans, by rising diversity of metazoan clades and by turnovers among lower and higher taxonomic levels, as extinctions removed many classes and (evidently) some phyla that had originated during the earlier period of explosive body-plan diversification. Remaining clades diversified disproportionately, replacing the extirpated lineages and continuing to contribute to rising diversity levels. Trilobites and inarticulate brachiopods were prominent members of this first fauna.

The second phase, spanning the remainder of the Paleozoic Era, saw the dominance of articulate brachiopods, crinoids, and some other newly abundant taxa in benthic communities. Bambach (1977) has reviewed the evidence of species diversities in Phanerozoic communities, and has concluded that this phase displayed an increase in species "packing" (number of species per unit area of habitat) of about 50% over the first phase. The change from the first to the second phases, then, was evidently accompanied by a restructuring of benthic ecosystems; these became significantly more complex. Finally, the late Permian extinctions brought the second phase to a close.

The succeeding third phase represents the fauna that rose to dominance following the Permian extinctions. This fauna is characterized by gastropods, bivalves, crustaceans, fishes, echinoids, and by other clades. Bambach's data suggest that the recovery from the low level of species diversity during the Permo-Triassic interval doubled the within-community diversity of the second phase (thus tripling that of the first phase). Despite the revolutions in benthic community composition and structure that occurred during changeovers between phases, there was no dramatic increase in the anatomical complexity of organisms to rival the increase that occurred early in the first phase.

4. Phanerozoic Patterns in the Continental Record

a. Vascular Land Plants

Nonmarine environments were probably colonized by prokaryotes and perhaps by autotrophic eukaryotes long before the rise of vascular plants, but actual fossil indications of any such invasions are few and are disputed. The oldest known vascular land plants lived during the Silurian period, more than 200 myr after the appearance of the earliest known marine metaphytes. The subsequent episodic diversifications and changes in floral composition

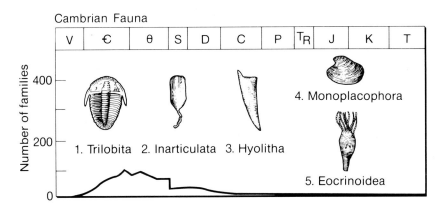

Figure III-7.— *The three great evolutionary faunas of the marine fossil record. Representatives of the most important classes within each fauna are shown, and diversity curves show the total number of families in each class (compare to cumulative diversity curve in fig. III-4). Sources of drawings: 1, 2, 6, 7, 8, 11, 13, 14, 16, 18, 20 after Moore et al. (1952); 3, 5, 9, 10, 15, 17, 19 after Fenton and Fenton (1958); 4, 12 after Teichert et al. (1953-81); and 21-24 after Romer (1966).*

40

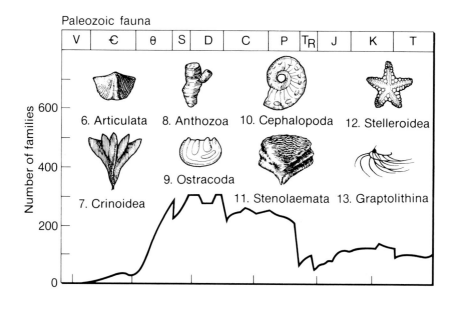

Paleozoic fauna

Number of families

| V | € | θ | S | D | C | P | T_R | J | K | T |

6. Articulata   8. Anthozoa   10. Cephalopoda   12. Stelleroidea

9. Ostracoda

7. Crinoidea   11. Stenolaemata   13. Graptolithina

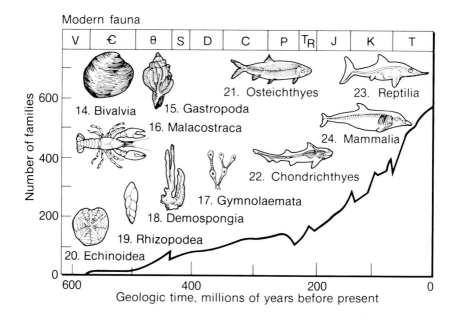

Modern fauna

Number of families

| V | € | θ | S | D | C | P | T_R | J | K | T |

14. Bivalvia   15. Gastropoda   21. Osteichthyes   23. Reptilia

16. Malacostraca   24. Mammalia

17. Gymnolaemata   22. Chondrichthyes

18. Demospongia

19. Rhizopodea

20. Echinoidea

Geologic time, millions of years before present

among vascular plants are similar to those seen in marine meta-zoans, as shown by a factor analysis of species-level data for land plants (Niklas et al., 1983). Four distinctive components can be identified (fig. III-8):

(1) A Silurian-Lower Devonian proliferation of early vascular plants that were characterized by a simple and presumbaly primitive morphology

(2) A subsequent Upper Devonian-Carboniferous radiation of derived plant lineages, some of which (including pteridophytes) achieved treelike proportions and heterospory

(3) An upper Devonian appearance of seed plants and their subsequent radiation culminating in a gymnosperm-dominated Mesozoic flora

(4) The appearance and rise of the flowering plants in Cretaceous through Tertiary time.

Three of these four phases of land plant evolution were associated with significant increases in the total number of species of land plants. The first occurred within a 60-myr period between the appearance of the first vascular plants and the decline of the earliest lineages, when the diversity of land plants increased four-fold. The second, involving the adaptive radiation of upper Devonian pteridophytes, resulted in another four-fold increase in species numbers by the Permian period. The third and last expansion of land plant diversity, resulting in a two-fold increase in species numbers, occurred by Neogene time and resulted from the proliferation of the angiosperms.

Although the appearance and radiation of the gymnosperms was associated with a pronounced decline in seedless plants, it did not result in a significant increase in the species richness of the world floras. This apparent exception to a pattern of increasing species diversity with each adaptive radiation may have resulted in part from the fact that some gymnosperm clades exploited "upland" habitats and were therefore seldom fossilized in the more commonly preserved major lowland depositional sites of the Carboniferous period. If so, perhaps the number of plant species did increase when the gymnosperms experienced their major radiation. However, a clear turnover from a pteridophyte-dominated to a gymnosperm-dominated flora occurred by the Permian period, suggesting that the disappearance of pteridophyte species compensated for the increase in gymnosperm species. If this

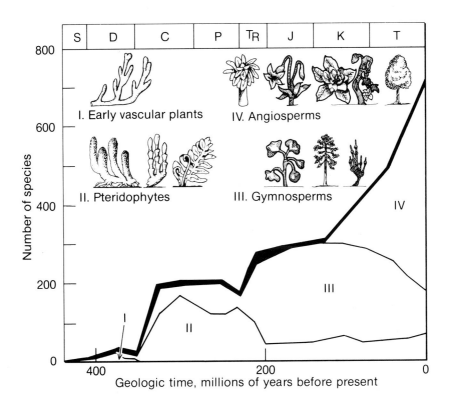

Figure III-8.— *Four groups of vascular plants have successively dominated terrestrial flora. The plants of each group share a common structural and/or reproductive grade. Following the invasion of land by primitive tracheophytes (group I), the remaining three groups successively replaced each other, with the radiation of each group terminating the dominance of its predecessor. Each radiation resulted in a major compositional change in the terrestrial flora, and in the cases of groups II and IV, a major increase in tracheophyte diversity. The transition from group II to group III is unique in its coincidence with an interval of major change in the physical environment. Solid black line at the top of the graph represents nonvascular land plants and plant fossils whose affinities are uncertain.*

numerical relationship is an accurate representation of events at that time, then no real increase in the number of plant species accompanied the gymnosperm radiation.

Based on the rate of appearance of new species and their durations within various clades of vascular plants, two distinctive patterns in tracheophyte evolution are evident:

43

(1) With a few exceptions, evolution *within* suprageneric clades begins with species with relatively short durations and high origination rates, and is followed by a progressive decrease in speciation rates and an increase in species durations

(2) Evolution *among* successively occurring suprageneric clades results in an increase in mean species origination rates and a decrease in mean species durations.

These tendencies are shown in figure III-9. In accordance with this pattern, the earliest vascular land plants (rhyniophytes and zosterophyllophytes) have longer species durations (12 to 14 myr) and lower species origination rates (0.04 to 0.07 species/myr) than do most other complex plant clades. Subsequently evolving pteridophyte and seed plant groups show increased mean species origination rates and decreased mean durations. The angiosperms, in contrast to the earliest tracheophytes, show the highest speciation rates and the lowest species durations. Even if the apparent "short species durations" of the angiosperms eventually prove to be an artifact of observing only their initial evolutionary phase of radiation, their substantially higher species origination rates stand in marked contrast to those of all other clades.

b. Land Animals

The continental metazoan fossil record has not been analyzed as thoroughly as has that of the marine biota. It is generally believed that the land record is less complete and therefore is less indicative of total faunal evolution than is the record of the shallow marine realm. For many continental groups (the insects, amphibians, reptiles, and early mammals, for example) observed patterns of diversity through time are influenced by the uneven quality of the fossil record as well as by important evolutionary events. As a result, the overall trends in the records of these groups are punctuated by a fine structure of detail that probably represents, in some cases, rare instances of exceptional conditions for fossilization rather than real changes in faunal diversity (fig. III-10). Although it is likely that some wormlike phyla were early land dwellers, the earliest fossilized land animals are arthropods. No new metazoan phyla, and only a few new classes, originated on land.

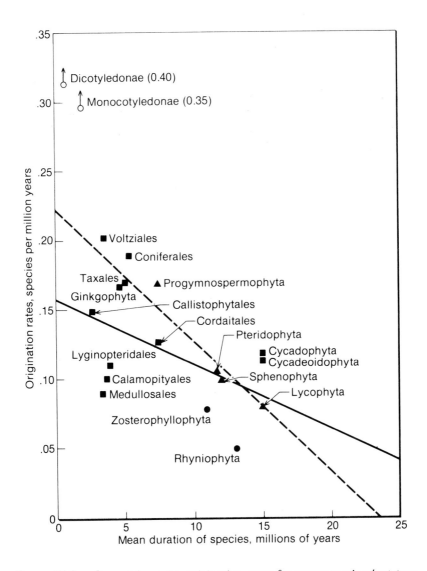

Figure III-9.— *Summed species origination rates for suprageneric plant taxa versus mean species duration of the same suprageneric taxa. The oldest taxa (rhyniophytes, zosterophyllophytes, lycophytes) have the lowest species origination rates and the longest species durations. The most recent taxa (monocotyledonae, dicotyledonae) have the highest origination rates and some of the shortest durations. The dotted line indicates a linear regression of origination rates versus durations for all groups plotted (r = 0.47); the solid line is a regression of the same data, but excluding monocotyledonae and dicotyledonae (r = 0.49). Suprageneric groups represented by dots belong to group I of figure III-8, those represented by triangles belong to group II, those represented by squares belong to group III, and those represented by open circles belong to group IV. Vertical axis: new species per taxon per million years. Horizontal axis: average species duration per taxon.*

Cenozoic

Mesozoic

Paleozoic

10
families
⊢――⊣

Figure III-10.– *Erratic detail in continental fossil record (insects) due to vagaries of preservation. The observed overall increase in the number of fossil insect families from the Paleozoic to the Cenozoic era is probably real, but the irregular smaller-scale pattern of expansion and decline probably reflects only the scattered occurrences of exceptional fossil-bearing deposits (for example, Mazon Creek siderite concretions, Solnhofen limestone, and Baltic amber).*

The earliest nonmarine vertebrates were fishlike animals, and the earliest tetrapod (four-legged) vertebrates evolved in the late Devonian period. The diversity of nonmarine vertebrates quickly increased to plateau levels that persisted throughout the remainder of the Paleozoic era (fig. III-11). Recent interpretations of the available record suggest sharp declines in vertebrate familial diversity at the ends of the Permian and Triassic periods (fig. III-11), although these could be artifacts of sampling. Neither of these apparent extinction events greatly altered long-term trends in vertebrate diversity. The greatest change occurred after the terminal Cretaceous extinction event, which was followed by the great radiations of mammals and birds in the Cenozoic era.

The fossil diversity of insects and other nonmarine arthropods is too poorly known and too highly influenced by spotty preservation to be a reliable indicator of their evolution. Arthropod diversity appears to decrease dramatically at the ends of the Carboniferous and Permian periods (fig. III-11) and to undergo lesser fluctuations at later times. The diversity of terrestrial arthropods also appears to increase markedly in the Cenozoic era, although this might be an artifact caused by a single fabulously wealthy fossil deposit — the Baltic amber of Northern Europe. In all of these cases, caution in interpretation is necessary.

As was the case with marine invertebrates, many of the basic patterns of morphological complexity of tetrapods were achieved during their early radiation. Thereafter the most striking departures in morphology were associated with the evolution of flight and of fully aquatic modes of life. With the increasing fragmentation of continents during the late Phanerozoic and the successive rise to dominance of new physiological grades (reptiles, perhaps dinosaurs, certainly mammals and birds), familial diversity, particularly among organisms of the late Cretaceous period and the Cenozoic era, increased. In addition, physiological advances produced organisms that eventually evolved individual intelligence and culture.

The history of terrestrial vertebrates, like that of the marine invertebrates, appears to be characterized by low persistent "background" extinction rates, and by occasional interruption by

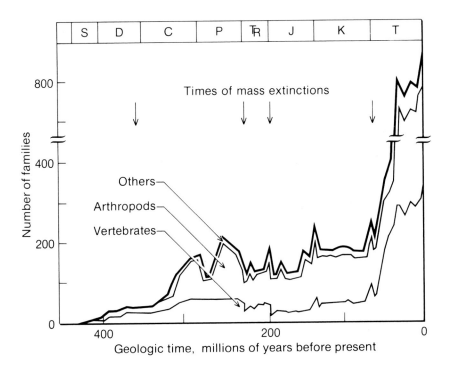

Figure III-11.— *Increase in diversity of nonmarine animals with time. Lower curve depicts vertebrates; width of center area represents arthropods. Upper curve shows total number of families, including protozoans and mollusks. Arrows show times of four of the five mass extinctions discussed in text.*

47

episodes of mass extinction. There appears to be some correspondence between marine and continental extinction events, but correlation of their timings and amplitudes is a matter of debate. For example, the terminal Permian extinctions on land do not appear to have been as extreme as were those in the ocean (Pitrat, 1973; compare figs. III-11 and III-4). The extinctions of dinosaurs, other large continental vertebrates, and some smaller animals were approximately contemporaneous with those of members of the marine biota. Large terrestrial vertebrates again suffered mass extinctions near the ends of the Eocene and Pleistocene epochs, with the latter extinction, now aggravated by human activity, continuing to the present. Both of these events (disregarding effects of human activities insofar as is possible in the latter instance) may have counterpart extinctions of moderate severity in the oceans (Sepkoski, 1982).

Many questions remain unanswered about large-scale rates of evolution of complex organisms and ecosystems, both on land and in the sea. For example, with only one fossil record, we do not know whether three-quarters of a billion years is a highly probable or a very aberrant time span for the evolution of intelligent organisms, or whether this time span would be shortened or lengthened if the Earth had not experienced large-scale replacement of taxonomic groups or major mass extinctions. (A tentative approach to these two questions is being considered by D. A. Russell.) Lacking answers at present, we can only speculate on the effects of chance events on the history of life. As an example, we might imagine that the removal of two apparently unnecessary time lags in the evolutionary history of continental biotas (namely, the 200-myr lag between the appearance of marine metaphytes and that of terrestrial tracheophytes, and the 100-myr lag between the appearance of mammals and the radiation of modern mammalian orders) might have resulted in the appearance of a technological civilization during the Carboniferous period. Alternatively, a few more large-scale perturbations of global ecosystems might have produced a biotic history characterized mostly by rebounds from mass extinctions, perhaps delaying the development of civilization until a time far in the future (or preventing its development altogether). Without further study of the history of evolutionary rates and patterns, we can do little to constrain such speculations.

5. Summary of Patterns in the Evolution of Complex Organisms

(a) The appearance of complex multicellular organisms required the prior evolution of eukaryotic cells and of genetic regulatory mechanisms. These developments had their own origins in a prior history of earlier biochemical and organelle evolution, one that was six times longer than the entire subsequent history of complex life on Earth. It is conceivable that eukaryotic cells could have developed within a much shorter time span, had the physical history of Earth and the outcomes of many stochastic processes been different.

(b) The fossil record shows a burst of metazoan evolution in the oceans during a 125-myr interval encompassing the Vendian interval (latest Precambrian) and the early Cambrian period. In that interval we see the appearance of soft-bodied acoelomate and coelomate animals, followed by that of skeletonized coelomates shortly thereafter. As near as we can tell, virtually all phyla evolved by the end of this interval, including those whose modern representatives are considered to possess some sort of intelligence. These latter are the mollusks (oldest fossils at 575 myr), the arthropods (oldest definite fossils at 570 myr), and the chordates (oldest fossils at 540 myr).

(c) Major bursts of evolution such as that seen in the early Cambrian period were repeated in other settings at other times during the Phanerozoic eon. For example, all major groups of vascular plants (except angiosperms) evolved within about 125 myr of the first appearance of tracheophytes on land. At lower taxonomic levels, most modern orders of mammals appeared in the 10- to 15-myr interval following the Cretaceous extinction of dinosaurs. The common pattern in these episodic evolutionary bursts of complexity seems to have been the appearance of one or several new organisms in an essentially empty ecological setting (Vendian metazoans in the sea, Ordovician or Silurian metaphytes on land, Tertiary mammals on land uninhabited by other large quadrupeds); these appearances were then followed by a rapid proliferation of forms derived from these organisms.

(d) Much of evolution subsequent to these bursts seems to have involved the elaboration of established patterns (as, for example, multiplication of species within established higher taxa) rather than the establishment of dramatically new patterns.

Two major phenomena seen in the fossil record are

(1) Successive diversification of large suites of major taxa ("evolutionary faunas" and "floras") with replacement of previously dominant taxa

(2) Periodic elimination of taxa during episodes of mass extinction, followed by evolutionary radiation of new taxa

It is not clear whether the average complexity of organisms changes during the successive diversifications of the major taxa, or whether mass extinctions are important in delaying, accelerating, or resetting any such trends.

B. RESEARCH SUGGESTIONS AND RECOMMENDATIONS

The patterns in the history of life and the development of complexity, summarized briefly above, raise important questions of interpretation. Answers to these questions will enhance the understanding of some of the most fundamental processes of evolution and ecology. To a large extent, the answers would be of immediate help in addressing certain practical problems arising in our own biosphere, would bear heavily on questions concerning the evolution of complex and intelligent life elsewhere in the universe, and would seem to be attainable within the near future.

We have identified seven areas of scientific investigation, wherein research would contribute greatly toward answers to these important questions. These areas are

(1) Accumulation, storage, retrieval, and evaluation of paleontological data

(2) Study of the biologic and environmental factors that led to the development of multicellularity

(3) Study of patterns and processes of evolutionary diversification, focusing on the late Precambrian-early Cambrian events which generated most living phyla and on subsequent patterns and rates of expansion and partitioning of global ecosystems

(4) Investigation of extinction patterns that reflect changing habitability of the prehistoric Earth and which can be relevant to changes that are occurring today

(5) Utilization of past extraterrestrial events that have left global time lines or benchmarks, to investigate ecological and biogeographic states of the biosphere within narrow slices of past time

(6) Exploration of new methods for studying the morphology of early body plans, such as through digital image enhancement of early fossil impressions

(7) Exploration of methods for the definition, measurement, and comparison of complexity in biological systems of all kinds

Recommendation 1. Fossil Data Storage and Retrieval

The highest priority in the area of paleontology is assigned to the construction of a data system adequate for the compilation, storage, and efficient manipulation of published information about the temporal and spatial occurrence of fossil organisms. Our current understanding of important features of the evolution of life on Earth (for example, our knowledge of the details of major patterns of diversification or of mass extinction episodes) has been derived from the published record only with great difficulty. To recognize important patterns, it is now necessary for researchers to review an enormous amount of published literature and to prepare indexes manually. One result is that most evolutionary patterns have been studied only at familial or higher levels (table III-1). This practice, born of necessity, introduces biases that may distort or even mask important evolutionary patterns among species, the basic unit of evolution.

There are a number of additional difficulties with making such inventories manually. Huge numbers of fossil species and genera have been described (table III-1), making any manual data storage system (such as a card file) unwieldy to the point of impracticality. Furthermore, additional records often cannot easily be added (depending upon the nature of the card file or other device employed), and errors, detected subsequently, cannot easily be removed. Changes in the identification of individual taxa cannot generally be accommodated; neither can new synonymies or changes in the hierarchical positions of individual taxa. But changes of these kinds may readily affect the outlines of the overall patterns and the ways in which they are presented and interpreted. A serious problem from the standpoint of paleontology, changes in the ages given to individual beds or stages cannot be taken into account easily or readily cross-indexed to individual records. Finally, data assembled for one purpose (for instance, for plotting the time occurrence of families) cannot easily be used for another purpose (such as determining the geographical distribution of families).

As a result of these difficulties, paleontologists who work with patterns generally extract information laboriously from a wide array of literature for a single purpose, consuming a great deal of valuable time, running the risk of introducing errors, and inevitably overlooking a great deal of valuable literature. The broader and more generally interesting the patterns may be, the less likely it is that an individual investigator will be able to accumulate information and subsequently detect errors. One negative consequence of the necessity of manually sorting fossil data is evident: although the Alvarez team has presented an impressively documented argument that a large object collided with the Earth 65 myr ago, years will elapse before paleobiologists can confirm or refute the idea that this impact was contemporaneous with certain of the extinctions that occurred at that time. The primary causes of this delay are the extreme dispersion in the literature of the biological and paleontological data needed to test this hypothesis, and the necessity to manually assemble these data. In general, the enormous amount of paleontological literature greatly impedes our ability to investigate this or any of the other effects that large-scale extraterrestrial phenomena may have had on the course of evolution on Earth.

This situation could be rectified with modern information-processing equipment and techniques, and with a team of scientists and technicians who could compile the data. The resultant data bank would make possible great gains in our understanding of the factors contributing to the pattern of diversification of life on Earth. For example, we could immediately calculate the representation of phyla, classes, genera, or any other taxonomic units in time, sum these data in any way desired, and determine the known spatial distribution of any group at any critical point in time. We could quickly reassign ages for strata as they are more precisely identified, remove or flag doubtful records, and update the data base in other ways. Pertinent environmental, biological, or morphological information could be added to the data base for the individual taxa, strata, or localities represented. This, in principle, would permit us to rapidly answer questions such as, "Which organisms became extinct in the interval immediately before or after formation of a large meteor crater?" "How is the number of genera of bivalve mollusks in existence at any given time correlated with the mean ocean temperature?" "How has taxonomic or morphologic complexity changed within a specific clade or circumscribed geographic area?" The appearance of selected features and combinations of features in the geological record could be read directly, and correlated with environmental or evolutionary events known to have occurred at the same time, or during preceding or subsequent intervals.

Entering at least some of the features of organisms into the data base would also greatly facilitate direct comparisons of modern and fossil organisms. Fossil pollen and spores, for example, are assigned to "form genera," which can be compared with their modern counterparts only through shared combinations of anatomical features. Such correlations and identifications could be made readily if the features were computerized along with the names. With such features, the data base would become valuable to paleontologists worldwide, who might respond by adding to (and correcting) the information in the base.

Although such a program is ambitious, the annual cost of maintaining it would not exceed the annual costs of today's more or less inefficient literature searches by paleontologists, especially those concerned with the kinds of broad-scale problems of interest to NASA. We must simplify the task of data storage so that retrieval and correlation can be easily accomplished. Now and in the future only the application of modern electronic data processing tools can effect the potential of the efforts made thus far to build our data base to its present level.

Recommendation 2. The Origin of Multicellularity

Although we cannot be sure of this generalization for other planets, it appears that (on Earth, at least) multicellularity is a prerequisite for the evolution of complex life. Since all multicellular organisms are composed of eukaryotic cells, we infer that it is necessary for life to become eukaryotic before it can become multicellular. The inverse of this view (that prokaryotic cells apparently cannot achieve multicellularity) deserves considerable study. Here, however, we confine ourselves to the evolution of multicellularity, once eukaryotic cells are available.

The genetic and developmental processes contributing to the evolution of multicellularity from single eukaryotic cells are of special interest in establishing the understanding of complex life and its origins. It is also desirable, in this context, to investigate the relative timing of the events in geologic history that led to multicellularity, as a means to infer the probabilities and conditions under which complex life can evolve from simpler forms.

Multicellularity need not lead to the rapid development of additional categories of biologic complexity. Multicellular animals and plants appeared well before Phanerozoic time, but they did not immediately give rise to forms of higher complexity. Plants, for example, did not evolve the parenchymal system essential for survival on land until about 400 myr ago. We are not aware of efforts to identify the factors that initiated this increase in structural complexity or other factors that might have delayed it. We know that the timing of certain historical events was limited by specific conditions. For example, vertebrates were not able to establish a permanent presence on land before atmospheric oxygen levels were suitable for breathing, and before a sufficient biologic opportunity (that is, food in the form of plants and invertebrates) became available there. But such prerequisites are not immediately obvious in the case of the development of multicellularity, and they bear further investigation.

It is equally important to understand the ways in which multicellularity evolved from a strictly biologic standpoint. Cytologic, physiologic, and genetic aspects of cellular differentiation are integrally related to multicellularity and the cell specializations that can follow. Typical questions in this area are

(a) What distinguishes colonial organisms (e.g., sponges) from multicellular organisms?

(b) What distinguishes filamentous and pseudoparenchymatous organisms from parenchymatous organisms?

(c) What are the epigenetic processes that lead to cellular differentiation?

(d) What environmental features influence the morphogenesis of multicellular organisms, and how do they exert their effects?

54

The possible effects of extraterrestrial and planetary factors on the evolution and survival of multicellular forms are mostly unknown. Are certain modes of multicellular construction sensitive to (or tolerant of) catastrophic changes in the environment? Are genetic processes that lead to multicellularity accelerated or decelerated by sudden changes in the environment? What influence, if any, does the strength of the gravitational field have upon the development of multicellularity? Certain of these questions can be addressed by experimental manipulation of multicellular organisms in conditions of varying environmental stress that simulate extraterrestrial influences.

To summarize, the origin of multicellularity was crucial to the origin of complex life on Earth, and may be equally critical to the development of life elsewhere in the universe. We recommend that the reasons for its long delay in occurrence, the genetic, cellular, and environmental factors that contributed to its appearance, and its relationship to extraterrestrial influences be investigated.

Recommendation 3. Diversification

a. Late Precambrian-Early Cambrian Diversification

The relatively sudden diversification of higher taxa during the late Precambrian-early Cambrian interval has been described as the greatest single episode of increase in morphological complexity in the history of life. Those diversification events that can be most closely delimited in time appear to occur at rates of evolutionary change that are higher than would be predicted from population genetic theory. Establishment of a data bank and subsequent refinement of information on the Precambrian-Cambrian diversification should sharpen our understanding of its pattern. Nevertheless, with reference to the overall evolution of complexity, it is already clear that this unique diversification of so many phyla and classes deserves special attention. Study of the functional morphology of the characteristic advanced features displayed by these early organisms; of their ecology (primitive feeding habits, primitive habitats, etc.); and of their interrelations and probable ancestries is of high priority. The mechanisms governing the timing of this unprecedented radiation also need continued study.

b. *Phanerozoic Pattern of Ecospace Occupation*

The Precambrian-Cambrian and subsequent diversifications tended to raise the number of species in the biosphere. How these additional forms are accommodated is an interesting question of relevance to our topic. If new species merely partitioned the adaptive zones or niches occupied by older lineages, then true novelties (which might include more complex forms) would not be expected to arise. However, there is some evidence (see fig. III-5) that the increase in diversity often involved invasion of new ecospaces. Research into this pattern and into the taxonomic consequences of such expansive evolution is recommended.

c. *Community Evolution*

The most appropriate modern analogs of the evolution of communities in the past should be studied because of the light they might shed on the evolution of complex life on Earth. Colonizations of remote oceanic islands (as for example the Hawaiian archipelago) and the subsequent diversifications of the island biotas provide a parallel to the recovery of a severely depleted world biota (such as occurred after the end of the Permian Period) following a global return to more favorable environmental conditions. Parallel evolution of communities (as for example in hot springs at similar temperatures that are on different continents, or in deserts formed independently on different continents) likewise provides valuable analogs that have historical precedents. These phenomena deserve closer scrutiny.

Recommendation 4. Extinctions and the Habitability of the Earth

We know little about the causes of mass extinctions, the patterns of normal "background" extinction, or the responses of different types of organisms to the stresses that cause extinction. The recent compilation of familial extinction rates by Raup and Sepkoski (1982) shows that the rates of extinction during the five largest episodes of mass extinction really were statistically higher than at other times, whereas the average rates of background extinction have apparently decreased with time, at least in the oceans (fig. III-6). Within this overall trend of decreasing background extinction rates, however, there may be other, shorter-term trends that are not adequately revealed by present data. For instance (although the data are not sufficiently accurate to claim such a conclusion at present), background extinction rates appear to rise during the intervals preceding the Permian, Triassic, and Cretaceous episodes of mass extinction. The refinement of our understanding of extinction in general and of the responses of organisms to the various forces of extermination that are likely to have influenced life and the geologic record is badly needed. Particular aspects of research of greatest relevance to understanding the relationship between extinction and complex life are

(1) Monitoring the progress of the modern mass extinction event

(2) Characterizing the five great mass extinctions and the 10 or more lesser mass extinctions (Sepkoski, 1982) of the past

(3) Increasing the taxonomic and stratigraphic resolution related to both background extinctions and mass extinctions, particularly for terrestrial ecosystems

a. The Modern Mass Extinction

Extinction of contemporary organisms is perhaps the most prominent feature of world ecosystems at present. Data available for estimating the impact of this extinction are preliminary, at best, although the distribution of known and named species provides one approach to this problem. There are approximately 1.5 million named species of living organisms. About two-thirds of these occur in temperate regions, and most of the rest are tropical. A reasonable estimate of the true total number of temperate species, based upon the results of contemporary revisionary studies, would be 1.5 million species. For well-known groups of organisms such as butterflies, certain other groups of insects, and vertebrates, there are at least twice as many species in the tropics as in temperate regions. The relationships between these figures suggest a world total of at least 4 to 5 million kinds of organisms, no more than a third of which have been studied and named.

The rapid growth of human populations in the tropics, coupled with high levels of poverty, indicates that virtually all tropical vegetation, worldwide, will be disturbed or even physically destroyed within the next 50 yr. Many of the plants, animals, and microorganisms of tropical forests are unable to reproduce except in undisturbed forest, a dependency that has led to predictions of the extinction of as many as a quarter of all living species on Earth within the next several decades. Such an event would probably exceed the terminal Cretaceous event in its magnitude of extinction and might, during the next several centuries or millenia, approach the dimensions of the extinction that occurred near the Permo-Triassic Boundary. Thus, the dimensions of prehistoric periods of extinction and the ways in which the world biota recovered from them are of particular interest for future human occupation of a stable world.

Presently there are no more than 4,000 taxonomists in the world capable of making professional determinations of organisms. Only 1,500 are capable of dealing with tropical organisms (U.S. National Research Council, 1980). There is, therefore, no possibility of classifying and naming a large proportion of the unstudied species before they become extinct. In terms of general human knowledge, and with specific reference to the measurement of rates of extinction, it will be necessary to devise coarse-resolution methods of sampling regional diversities of organisms (similar to the techniques now routinely employed by meteorologists, for example) and to use these methods to estimate, with much more precision than is now possible, the total biomass and diversity of the living biota and the rate at which species are becoming extinct. The need is acute for terrestrial organisms and is particularly acute for tropical organisms.

The monitoring of these changes has great importance for human prospects, as well as for the scientific understanding of the global extinction problems posed above. For the detection of gross changes in ecosystems, NASA satellite capabilities are particularly appropriate. Ground studies of the responses of the species that survive the destruction of the Amazon rain forest, for example, may provide clues as to the origins of the evolutionary radiations that followed the mass extinctions of the past. Evolutionary considerations aside, endangerment of the majority of the Earth's land plants and animals could have serious consequences for the future habitability of our planet. Careful surveillance and analysis is both necessary and compatible with NASA's incipient "Habitability of the Earth" program.

b. The Five Great Mass Extinctions of the Past

Immense mass extinctions of the marine biota occurred in the late Ordovician, the late Devonian, the late Permian, the late Triassic and the late Cretaceous periods. Although many causes have been suggested for each, none has been unequivocally demonstrated. Large perturbing events synchronous with these extinctions are known only for two of them (glaciation and sea level change in the late Ordovician period and a possible large-body impact, indicated by a geologic "iridium spike," at the end of the Cretaceous period). Not only are causative agents unknown, but the range of taxa surviving, the taxa actually exterminated, and precise temporal sequences are not adequately understood in any case. Thus, the causes of these extinctions and their effects on the history of life on Earth cannot yet be fully assessed. Each of these extinctions merits attention equal to that now focused upon the terminal Cretaceous episode. From the standpoint of the whole biosphere, the three large Paleozoic mass extinctions were each more profound than was the terminal Cretaceous event. Each event may have had a different cause and a different influence upon life.

The five great mass extinctions might represent one end of a spectrum of events whose severities grade smoothly from the extreme represented by, say, the Permian extinction to the rather constant low-level effects seen as a result of "normal" background extinction. At least 10 other lesser mass extinctions have been identified in the marine fossil record (fig. III-12): five in the Cambrian period, three in the Mesozoic era, and two in the Cenozoic era. It is entirely possible that more such events, of comparable or lesser severity, will be discovered, especially in the long interval between the Cambrian and Permian periods. Tentative suggestions of small extinction events in the early Ordovician and late Silurian periods are, in fact, already discernible. All of these lesser extinctions need to be fully documented, both by description of their nature and intensity and by delineation of their

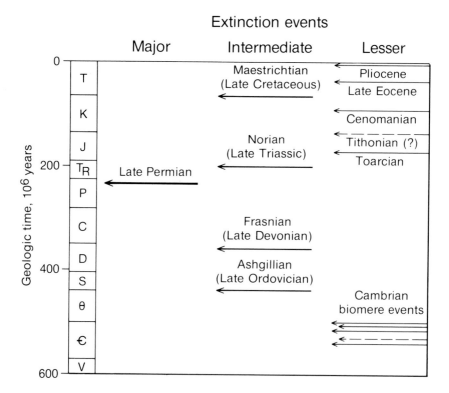

Figure III-12.— *Distribution of known mass extinctions through Phanerozoic time. The five mass extinctions discussed in the text are shown here as events of "major" and "intermediate" severity. Approximately 10 minor ("lesser") episodes of mass extinction that did not severely depress familial diversity have been recognized to date; this number may increase with further exploration of the marine fossil record. (From Sepkoski, "Mass Extinctions in the Phanerozoic Ocean: A Review," Geological Society of America, Special Paper 190, pp. 283-289.)*

distributions in time. It is also important to determine whether the mechanisms underlying these events, and others of low severity, were qualitatively different from those that caused very high extinction rates, and from those that contribute to normal background extinctions.

c. Background Extinction Rates and the Habitability of the Earth

The habitability of the surface of the Earth may fluctuate with time for a variety of reasons. These can include changes in solar

60

radiation, changes in rates of impact of extraterrestrial bodies, encounters with galactic dust resulting in changes in radiation levels as the solar system orbits the galaxy, and planetary changes related to lithospheric activity (plate motion, volcanism, major changes in the oxygen and carbon dioxide content of the atmosphere, etc.). Long-term trends in average or background extinction rates provide a possible monitor of such changes in the past habitability of the Earth. Present data are faintly suggestive, but are still inadequate for use in drawing firm conclusions about environmental changes of the past. More accurate and detailed data on extinction rates through time and in various habitats (e.g., the upper 10 m of the ocean) are required for the increased resolution needed to evaluate possible trends in the fluctuation of background extinction rates. Data at lower taxonomic levels (especially at the generic level) and with finer stratigraphic resolution (such as the zone level) could be compiled from the immense available literature as part of the compilation of a paleontological data base, or as a separate project. Invaluable insight into the nature of extinction, and of possible terrestrial and extraterrestrial phenomena that contribute to it, could be gained from a comprehensive data set with a degree of resolution that would permit examination of the fine structure of patterns in the history of extinction.

Recommendation 5. Utilization of Extraterrestrial Impacts as Data Planes in the Evolution of Complex Life

Anomalously high concentrations of the element iridium, found in many parts of the world near the Cretaceous-Tertiary and Eocene-Oligocene boundaries, are thought to represent impacts of large asteroids or other bodies of extraterrestrial origin. On impact these bodies disintegrated, producing great clouds of iridium-rich dust which are thought to have dispersed globally. Some workers (Alvarez et al., 1980) have argued that mass extinctions could be the direct result of the impacts. Although this hypothesis is still disputed (see, e.g., Archibald and Clemens, 1982), it has stimulated a great deal of creative research and discussion, and provides two major opportunities for further elucidation of events in Earth history.

First, the possibility of the direct contribution of meteor impacts to extinctions needs to be further studied. Second, the impacts of extraterrestrial bodies may provide datum planes that provide a hitherto impossible resolution of the records of the evolution of life. Methods of biostratigraphic, paleomagnetic, and radiometric determination of ages of deposits decrease in precision, in general, with increases in the ages of the deposits. Correlations of deposits formed some 70 myr ago usually have uncertainties measured in terms of hundreds of thousands or even millions of years. However, the impacts of extraterrestrial objects, which are essentially instantaneous events capable of leaving global geologic signatures generated within a few months or years, provide exceptional opportunities for charting ancient geographies and biogeographies with great resolution. By utilizing these global marker deposits, we could identify widely scattered fossils and sediments of both marine and terrestrial origin as representing times just before and just after each extraterrestrial event. Prerequisite to this line of investigation are operational criteria for recognizing and correlating traces of presumed extraterrestrial events across broad geographical areas and variable environments of deposition — traces that may have been affected by different post-depositional processes. If we had this knowledge at hand, pertinent records from the paleontological data bank could be ordered to show the nature and positions of the ancient continents and oceans and the makeups of regional biotas as they existed during an interval of a few months or years at that time. This interval is actually shorter than the time that would be needed to accomplish a similar survey of the modern biota, and is a million-fold improvement over the million-year or longer intervals used in current summaries of the organization and complexity of ancient biotas.

An example of how exploitation of iridium anomalies could be valuable in understanding evolution after an extinction can be drawn from the early history of higher primates. A zone of iridium enrichment has been found near the Eocene-Oligocene boundary (Alvarez et al., 1982; Ganapathy, 1982). If the iridium enrichment zone proves to be of worldwide distribution at this boundary, and if it seems to have been deposited essentially instantaneously over the surface of the Earth, it will provide the sort of time marker referred to above, allowing identification of deposits that were all formed within a year or two of each other. At about the time of the zone's formation, many groups of primitive primates disappeared from the record, and anthropoids made their appearance.

Increased resolution of the timing of these events and their contemporaneous courses on different continents would speak to questions concerning the times of origin of Old and New World monkeys as well as those of the apes and human ancestors. If, in addition, the iridium trace proved to be the signature of an asteroid collision with the Earth, then a doubly valuable understanding of the response of terrestrial life in general, and of the primates in particular, to such an event would be forthcoming.

Recommendation 6. Image Enhancement of Critical Fossils

Some NASA instrumentation is potentially valuable for the study of critical but poorly preserved fossils. Many of the oldest fossils of complex animals and plants are preserved in sandstones and coarse siltstones. This imposes a "graininess" on the fossil that has the effect of adding geological "noise" to the biological "signal" of interest. This noise impedes or prevents discernment of the fine-scale morphology of the fossils, which in turn reduces certainty of taxonomic assignment and morphological interpretation of these, the oldest animal and plant fossils.

NASA digital image technology may be useful for separating the geological noise from the biological signal and for enhancing the biological signal in a variety of kinds of fossils (Kirschvink et al., 1982). Fossils that might be investigated with this technology include the following:

(1) Ediacarian fossils. These oldest (600–670 myr) animal fossils, which occur in many localities around the world, are poorly understood in terms of both anatomy and taxonomic relationships. This is partially due to their preservation as impressions in coarse-grained sandstone (fig. III-3). Image enhancement may improve this situation, thus permitting better understanding of the early appearance of phyla and of the early evolution of complex animals.

(2) Vascular plant fossils. Old vascular plant fossils are often poorly preserved as dissociated fragments in coarse sediments; image enhancement could help us to visualize the morphology of these fragments and would aid our understanding of the early evolution of complex plants.

(3) Burgess Shale fauna. Fossils of the Cambrian Burgess Shale (525 myr) represent a variety of now-extinct phyla and

classes, with some soft-part anatomy variably preserved. Image enhancement could be an important aid for studying the morphology of these problematic animals.

(4) Terrestrial vertebrates. Many studies of the evolution, functional anatomy, and systematics of terrestrial vertebrates involve research on microscopic and frequently poorly preserved anatomical details such as wear facets on occlusal surfaces of teeth or the evolution of new articular surfaces between bones. Image enhancement techniques might provide new data on these minute structures.

Imaging equipment developed by NASA and various subsidiaries for such projects as planetary probe missions might be easily adapted to the analysis of the various fossil organisms noted above.

Recommendation 7. The Definition of Complexity

Although we have used the term "complexity" liberally, we have heretofore skirted its actual definition and the specification of its measurement. Complexity is such a difficult concept that we wish to recommend, as a separate research topic, the formulation of methods for conceptualizing and quantifying complexity for use with organisms and with the biosphere. In the literature, at least three definitions are commonly implicit in treatments of complexity of organisms. These are

(1) Diversity (simple numbers of taxa at some specified level) in some specified local or global region

(2) Measurements of the sophistication of organism morphology (interesting approaches are those of Cisne (1974), who measured increasing serial differentiation of limbs in arthropods, and of Niklas (1979, 1982), who computed relative complexities of living and fossil plant forms from their patterns of branching and apical development)

(3) Measures of genome size (Hinegardner, 1976) and gene coding, involving the notion of the information content required of genomes to code for organisms of different degrees of anatomical sophistication or differentiation

Additionally, one might suggest measures of the versatility of behavior or of intelligence as indicators of complexity. Some measures of complexity in the computer sciences might be modified to serve these and other purposes. Once an acceptable measure of complexity is devised, it could be applied to determine patterns in the development of complexities with respect to all of the other patterns — diversification, extinction, biogeography, etc. — noted above. We therefore recommend a study of the concept and definition of biotic complexity.

CHAPTER IV

PHYSICAL-CHEMICAL ENVIRONMENTS AND THEIR GEOLOGIC HISTORY

R. K. Bambach, A. G. Fischer, and R. M. Garrels

A. THE DYNAMIC EARTH

The Earth has changed continuously throughout its history and continues to be active today. Some of its most important changes occurred early in its history. These changes include the density differentiation of the structure of the Earth (including the formation of its crust, hydrosphere, and atmosphere) and the development of the composition of its atmosphere. The major features of these two developmental trends occurred during the Archaean and Proterozoic eras prior to the evolution of complex life (Fig. III-1), and may have been necessary developments for the creation of acceptable environments for the subsequent evolution of complex life.

Environmental changes have been continuous during the last 300 myr, and have been characterized by variation without any single constant direction. They have operated at durations ranging from 24 hr to 10^8 yr. In particular, plate tectonic activity has contributed a major share of this ongoing environmental shakeup. Movements of the continents have caused long-term sea-level fluctuations, changes in the areas of shallow marine and continental habitats, regional climatic shifts, alteration of the geographic continuity of oceans and continents, and uplifts of mountain ranges. Other environmental changes have included the onsets of glacial and thermal intervals, effects due to perturbations of the Earth's magnetic field, and variations in atmospheric and oceanic chemistries. The causes of many of these environmental fluctuations are not well understood. Some are probably related to feedback mechanisms involving life processes, some to internal Earth dynamics (including the movements of the continents), and some to the influences of astronomical phenomena.

The constant change in conditions on the surface of the Earth is an important characteristic of the environment in which the evolution of complex life has taken place. These changes, which include the effects of certain extraterrestrial factors discussed in chapter VI, have provided stimuli for the biological evolution described in chapter III. It seems likely that a dynamic planet, providing new environmental opportunities for evolutionary innovation and selective pressures that channel the further development of such innovations, is necessary as a setting for the evolution of complex life. At the same time, we may hypothesize that planets with inert or slowly changing surfaces, and others upon which change is rapid, dramatic, ceaseless, or unidirectional, might be less suitable for the evolution of complex life. In the former case, the absence of disturbances capable of causing mass extinctions, or of opening new isolated habitats for colonization and speciation, might allow the long-term occupation of the planet by a restricted suite of well-adapted organisms. These, as a consequence of their adaptations to the relatively stable conditions, may seldom disappear in numbers sufficient to leave a relatively unoccupied landscape, within which subordinate organisms of alternative designs might radiate and acquire additional complexity. This is the (unproven) "evolutionary stasis" condition, discussed in chapter V. At the other extreme, environmental change that is too rapid and severe may prevent the evolutionary development of all but the most rudimentary "complexity," by making it advantageous for organisms to remain small, to reproduce rapidly, and to avoid specialization for the exploitation of environmental opportunities that may quickly cease to exist. Although we cannot prove this hypothesis, we find it reasonable to expect some intermediate level of environmental disturbance and change to be optimal for the rapid evolution of complex life. With that hypothesis in mind, it is of interest to examine the many disturbances of the Earth's surface that have occurred within Phanerozoic and earlier time, and to relate their severity and frequency to important events in the evolution of complex biological organisms and communities.

1. Effects of Continental Movements

Because of certain flows of material in the Earth's interior, the "plates" residing at the surface are compelled to move. Certain of these massive plates contain parts of the modern continents, and the slow adjustments of the plates over the ages have caused the continents to change their positions and shapes. One consequence of this "continental drift" is that geographies of the ancient Earth bear little resemblance to today's geography (fig. IV-1). The motions of the plates (and the continents) have caused other continuous changes besides those occurring in the configurations of the oceans and the continents. The elevation of mid-oceanic ridges, the formation of deep sea trenches, changes in the volumes of ocean basins, fluctuations in sea level, and changes in the areas of shallow marine and continental habitats all follow from continental movements. The movements of continental blocks through various latitudes have altered the climates on their surfaces as they have moved from one zone to another, and interactions of plate margins have directly influenced their general topography by causing the folding and buckling that results in mountain formation. Some consequences of these changes are reviewed here.

a. Geographic Pattern and Continuity of Habitats

Half a billion years ago the continents were isolated blocks scattered around the equator, and the major ocean basins were centered on the poles (fig. IV-1a). During the next 250 myr these isolated continents came into contact to form the "supercontinent" of Pangaea (fig. IV-1e; Bambach et al., 1980, and references therein). Biogeographic relations constantly changed through this time span because of this plate motion (Scotese, 1979; see also Scotese et al., 1979; and Ziegler et al., 1983). Pangaea persisted for approximately 100 myr and then began to fragment. The modern geography, characterized by three north-south oriented

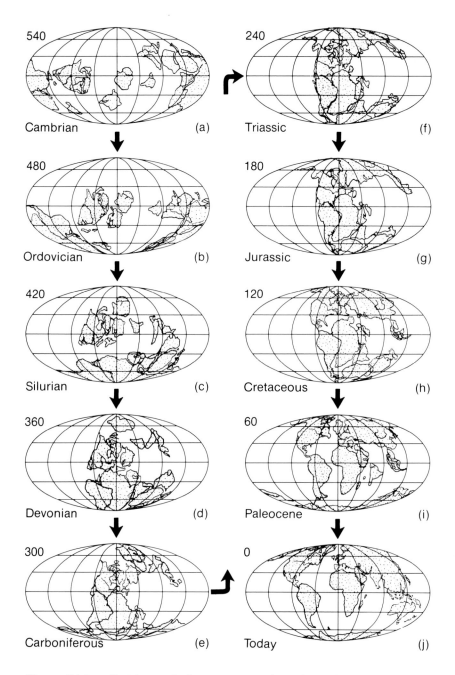

Figure IV-1.— *Positions of the continents throughout Phanerozoic time. Numbers show dates (millions of years in the past). (After Scotese, 1976, and Scotese et al., 1979).*

continental masses (the Americas, Europe-Africa, and Asia-Australia) with three semi-isolated large ocean basins (the Atlantic, Pacific, and Indian oceans) has developed only within the past 160 myr.

Geographic change plays a major role in determining the setting in which evolution occurs. During times of continental dispersion, the faunas of the continents and their adjacent shallow-shelfed seas evolve in isolation from each other. Distinctive biotas, such as the eucalyptus forest and marsupial terrestrial fauna of Australia, are the result. These distinctive biotas add to global diversity. At other times, when insularity is reduced by the collisions of the continents, independently evolved faunas and floras are forced into contact with each other. At such times, organisms find themselves in competition with species that they have never encountered before. The total diversity of species, genera, and even families has been lowered at such times by competitive elimination of species occupying similar niches. One well-documented example is the confrontation between North American and South American faunas when the Panamanian land bridge developed in Pliocene time (Simpson, 1960; Marshall et al., 1982). Although each continent retained the same internal diversity (because of the success of immigrant groups that replaced native forms), the total family level diversity for both continents combined dropped by 20%. Major biogeographic and evolutionary events of this sort, ultimately resulting from plate motion, take about 10^6 yr even though continental isolation and recombination itself operates on a time scale of about 10^8 yr.

b. Long-Term Sea-Level Fluctuations and Changes in Habitat Area

The major changes of sea level relative to that of the continents during the past 570 myr follow a bimodal pattern. Sea level was high in early Paleozoic time, dropped to about its present level in the late Paleozoic-Triassic interval, rose to a high level in the late Mesozoic-Paleogene interval, and then dropped to its present height (Vail et al., 1977; Hallam, 1977; fig. IV-2a). This general pattern of ancient changes can be detected both in North American formations and in those of the Soviet Union, although details differ from the two areas (fig. IV-2b, after Hallam, 1977). Although the present low sea level may be due in part to the large

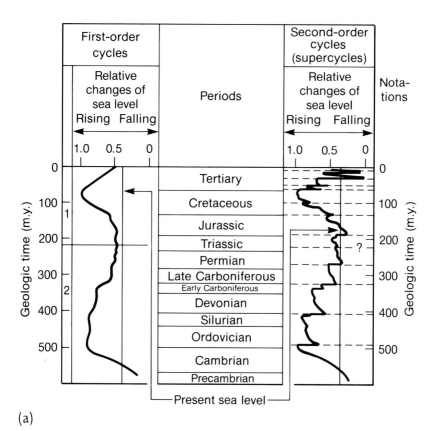

(a)

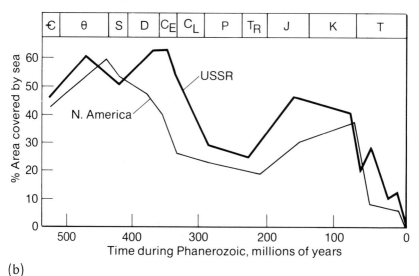

(b)

volume of ice stored on the Antarctic continent, these sea-level changes have probably resulted from the displacement of water caused by changes in ocean basin volume over most of Phanerozoic time. Changes in basin volume, in turn, have resulted from the growth and subsidence of mid-oceanic ridges and from continental collisions. Ocean basin volume decreases as mid-ocean ridges grow on the sea floor (when lithospheric plate motion is rapid). Water is displaced from the basins by the growth of the ridges, and sea level rises (Russell, 1968; Hays and Pitman, 1973). The sea level drops when the ocean basin volume increases because of the subsidence of mid-ocean ridges at times of slow plate motion. (Ocean basin volume can also increase if continental crustal area decreases, because of underthrusting in continental collisions.) Indirectly, then, plate motions are tied to changes in sea level (Fischer, 1981, 1982).

A drop in sea level to the edge of the continental shelf greatly reduces the area of shallow-water bottoms throughout the world and likewise increases the area of the land — in particular that of the coastal plains. A rise of sea level has the opposite effect, in decreasing lowland area and expanding the area of shallow seas. Since organisms occupying a shrinking habitat experience declining population sizes (perhaps with consequent extinctions), the motions of the plates may exert drastic indirect effects on shallow marine and coastal lowland communities, applied over long periods through the agency of sea-level change (T. J. Schopf, 1974; Simberloff, 1974). This effect may be particularly important for the shallow marine habitat, which can be restricted in area to a belt that is only a few tens of kilometers in width, extending around the perimeters of the continents at times of low sea level (such as during the late Permian period, early Triassic period, and Pleistocene epoch), or which can occupy up to half the total area

Figure IV-2.— *(Opposite) Changes in sea level over Phanerozoic time. (a) First-order changes (left) and estimated second-order changes (right), whole Earth. After Vail et al. (1977). (b) First-order changes, North America and U.S.S.R. (The present "% covered" is arbitrarily set at 0. However, a significant continental shelf area is presently submerged.) (After Hallam (1977).) (b) reprinted by permission from Nature, vol. 269, pp. 709-772, 1977. Copyright 1977, Macmillan Journals Limited.*

of the continental crust at times of high sea level (such as during the middle Silurian or late Cretaceous period; fig. IV-2a).

The onsets of ice ages, which may result from factors other than continental movement, may cause sea-level changes to occur more rapidly than do those resulting from plate tectonic activity. One cycle of continental glacier formation and melting, by withdrawing water from the seas, storing it as landlocked ice, then returning it, can lower and raise the average sea level of the Earth by a few tens of meters within a few thousand years. This occurred during the past million years (the Pleistocene ice ages), and even greater fluctuations may have been driven by the Carboniferous glaciations about 300 myr ago. During the Pleistocene Epoch, sea level dropped repeatedly to about 150 m below the present level during times of glacial advance and rose again to present (or higher) levels when the ice sheets melted during interglacial stages. By contrast, the oscillations of sea level associated with plate motion — those that occur as minor perturbations of the very-long-term bimodal pattern (the "wiggles" in the curve of fig. IV-2a) — repeat themselves every 10^7 yr or so. Such changes have stressed terrestrial, freshwater, and shoalwater biotas throughout Phanerozoic time, while leaving the deep ocean habitats largely unaffected.

c. Regional Climatic Changes

Many sediments deposited in ancient times reflect climates that are inappropriate for the latitudes in which these sediments are located today. For example, late Ordovician glacial deposits occur in northern Africa, tropical reefs occur in Silurian and Devonian deposits of the American midcontinent, the great tropical coal swamps of the Carboniferous occur in North America and Europe, Permian desert salt deposits occur in Germany, and Jurassic desert dune sands are found in Utah. These puzzles are partially resolved by assuming that the deposits formed at times when the lithospheric plates moved through latitudinal zones where those climatic conditions prevail. (The zones themselves may have shifted, relative to their present positions, as a consequence of past increases or decreases in mean global temperature.) The sediments are therefore products of the climatic regimes of the latitudinal belts into which those continents drifted in the past. These regional climatic influences, together with the past positions of the continents, affected oceanic circulation patterns and controlled faunal and floral distributions of the past (Scotese et al., 1979; Gray and Boucot, 1976).

d. Topographic Changes

Convergent plate margins are the sites of the formation of major mountain belts (the Himalayas, Alps, and Andes, and, in the distant past, the Urals and Appalachians; Dewey and Bird, 1970). Rifting plate margins form narrow deep basins (the Red Sea, the Gulf of California) and eventually cause flooding of continental margins (such as the Atlantic coast of North America; Watts and Steckler, 1979). Long-term fluctuation in habitat conditions, drainage patterns, and habitat variety is one result of the interactions of these plate margin processes with the surficial effects of erosion and sediment deposition. The Andean uplift, for example, created a great diversity of habitats lying right across the tropics, mainly during the past 20 myr. In this regard, South America is quite different from Africa, which has no major mountain range extending through the tropics. Perhaps as a consequence, South America is occupied by more species of birds, amphibians, and freshwater fishes than are found in Africa.

2. Environmental Changes Caused by Factors Other Than Continental Movements

Worldwide changes in physical and chemical environmental conditions include climatic change, changes in the Earth's magnetic field, and changes in atmospheric and oceanic composition. Causes for these changes are difficult to determine, partly because they are produced by combinations of factors rather than by single influences. World climatic conditions may be influenced by geographic, atmospheric, and (possibly) extraterrestrial phenomena. The magnetic field is produced by internal Earth processes that cannot be observed directly. Atmospheric and oceanic compositions are influenced by biological feedback systems, by direct physical and chemical feedback processes at the Earth's surface, and by small contributions from (and losses to) the interplanetary medium.

a. Climatic Change Over Phanerozoic Time

The origin and persistence of life shows that climatic extremes have never been severe enough to freeze or boil the entire biosphere during the last four billion years. Yet lesser climatic changes have occurred at varying scales and amplitudes. The Earth experiences annual changes in weather conditions that vary in severity with latitude. Long-term changes (on a scale varying from 10^4 to 10^5 yr) are recorded in the fluctuations of the Pleistocene ice sheets (Hays et al., 1976), and in the bedding cycles of sediments (Fischer, 1980; Schwarzacher and Fischer, 1982). Very-long-term fluctuations in world climate (on a scale of 3×10^8 yr) are punctuated by periods of widespread glaciation separated by long intervals during which even the poles seem to have been ice-free (fig. IV-3; Schwarzbach, 1963; Frakes, 1979).

The best evidence of nonglacial periods is for the last one, specifically that of Late Cretaceous, Paleocene, and Eocene time. Paleotemperature measurements obtained from Cretaceous surface-dwelling Foraminifera (Douglas and Savin, 1975) show that tropical sea surface temperatures were similar to those of today, and that relatively warmer waters occurred in high latitudes at that time. Temperatures determined for oceanic bottom waters from depths in the 4,000-m range (which are now at or below $3°C$) were around $14°C$ in Cretaceous to mid-Eocene times. This implies either that the deep waters of the past originated in arid tropical regions as a consequence of salinity increase via evaporation, or that the polar oceans were remarkably warm. Because cooler water is more dense and normally sinks to become the deep water of the ocean, it seems most probable that the polar areas were not cool.

A decrease in the temperature of deep ocean waters throughout the Tertiary period, with occasional minor reversals, marks the transition to the Pleistocene–Present world. Evidence of climatic cooling in the late Cenozoic is also shown by changes in floras and faunas. A huge fauna (over 300 species) of subtropical mollusks occurred near western Greenland in the Paleocene epoch (Kollmann, 1979). During the Eocene epoch, a moist subtropical

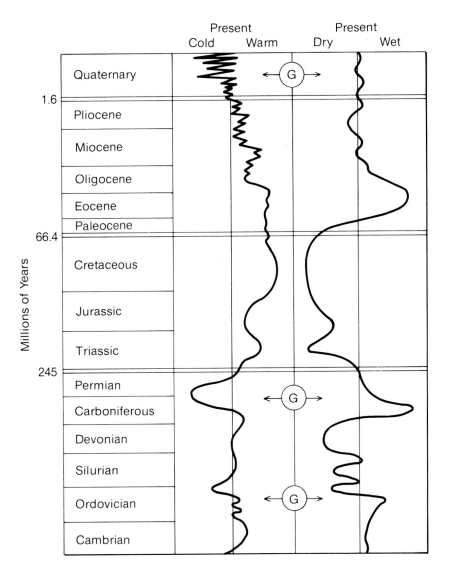

Figure IV-3.— *Changes in global temperature and precipitation throughout Phanerozoic time. Periods of widespread glaciation (arrows) occurred in the middle and late Ordovician, early Permian, and Quaternary periods, and about 100 myr before the beginning of the Cambrian period. Quarternary period shown much exaggerated here; other times not to scale. (After Frakes, "Climates Throughout Geologic Time," Elsevier, Amsterdam, 1979.)*

forest assemblage of plants and animals inhabited nearby Ellesmere and Axel Heiberg Islands, at paleolatitudes in excess of 55° (West and Dawson, 1978). Today these high-latitude regions have low-diversity cold-adapted biotas. Benson (1979) has documented the response of the deep-sea ostracods to the development of cold deep-sea waters during the Eocene and Oligocene epochs, and Stanley and Campbell (1981) have demonstrated the effect of decreased temperatures in Atlantic waters during the Plio-Pleistocene extinction.

Many proposals have been offered to explain the controlling factors of global climate and the causes of climatic change. Some have called upon astronomical variables, whereas others have invoked strictly terrestrial causes. Astronomical models depend upon differing intensities of solar radiation incident upon the Earth, possibly caused by changes in solar luminosity (Opik, 1952), interference with sunlight by interplanetary dust clouds (Schwarzbach, 1963), or variations in the Earth's orbital characteristics (Milankovitch, 1930, 1941; Imbrie and Imbrie, 1979). Other models invoke terrestrial factors as major influences on climatic change. The positions of polar land masses and the isolation and refrigeration of polar waters are emphasized as major climatic influences by Ewing and Donn (1956) and Crowell and Frakes (1970). Barron et al. (1981) stress albedo effects from land masses in the subtropical zones as a climate-forcing mechanism. Changes in the atmospheric abundance of volcanic dust and gases (such as CO_2) have been suggested as causes of climatic change (for example, Lamb, 1977; Bray, 1977; Schwarzbach, 1963). These effects may interact with others (such as the large-scale burial of organic matter) which affect the abundance of CO_2.

b. Changes in the Earth's Magnetic Field

The Earth's magnetic field, which changes in several ways, pervades the biosphere. Changes in magnetic inclinations and declinations, which occur quasi-cyclically and within limits, are called "secular variation." The strength of the field fluctuates through time, and the direction of the field undergoes reversals. These latter changes are of great significance to investigators of Earth history. The history of these reversals can be read in the magnetic anomalies of the deep-sea floor. The magnetic reversal history of

78

the last 800 myr is being assembled bit by bit through the study of stratigraphic sequences (McElhinney, 1973). Although the case for a coincidence of major extinction events with magnetic reversal patterns remains weak, recent work has shown that many organisms are sensitive to the magnetic field and have developed orienting (and other) responses to its presence. Decline of field strength or reversal of the field might therefore be detectable by certain members of organic communities and may initiate evolutionary responses, perhaps occurring throughout all habitats, as a possible consequence. As noted in chapter VI, the Earth's magnetic field acts as an important shield against cosmic radiation. At times when the field is reversing, its strength diminishes. Life on the Earth is particularly susceptible to disturbance (or destruction) by the radiation generated by nearby supernova explosions, if these occur at such times. At present, the coincidence of a nearby supernova and collapsed magnetic field is considered to be highly improbable. Planets with other stellar neighborhoods and/or magnetic characteristics might be more vulnerable to this combination of factors, however.

c. Changes in Atmospheric and Oceanic Oxygen Levels

At present, oxygen constitutes 20.9% of the atmosphere. Additions to atmospheric oxygen occur primarily by the photosynthetic activities of plants. Photosynthesis effectively splits water into two hydrogen atoms, which enter the biosphere in newly produced organic matter, and an oxygen atom that is combined with another and released to the hydrosphere or atmosphere as molecular O_2. In the process, carbon dioxide is also incorporated into organic matter. These oxygen additions to the atmospheric, hydrospheric, and organic reservoirs are balanced by withdrawals caused by respiration of organisms, combustion of organic matter, and rock weathering (primarily the oxidation of the iron sulfide mineral, pyrite).

Our knowledge of past levels of atmospheric oxygen is changing rapidly, but the following represents our understanding of the situation at this time. The atmosphere of the early Earth, before the time at which aerobic photosynthetic organisms evolved and before their activities became significant, is believed to have been essentially devoid of free oxygen. The generation of oxygen in those early millenia was mainly limited to the photodissociation of water (Berkner and Marshall, 1965). This process is generally considered to be insignificant, in comparison with global photosynthesis, as a potential contributor to atmospheric oxygen levels. The complete absence of oxygen in the ancient atmosphere has been questioned recently (Clemmey and Badham, 1982) but there is no evidence for abundant atmospheric oxygen before middle Proterozoic time. J. W. Schopf (1974) places the transition to an oxygen-bearing atmosphere at 1.8 billion years ago (fig. III-1). The oxygen-rich atmosphere of today is a direct result of organic photosynthesis (Cloud, 1976).

No direct measurements of atmospheric oxygen levels in the past can be made, but indirect approaches yield some information. In the present outer atmosphere, ultraviolet rays combine oxygen into ozone, and this ozone shields the Earth's surface from that radiation. Berkner and Marshall (1965) postulated that living things could not have invaded the continents without the protection provided by such a shield. If this is valid (see, for example, Rambler and Margulis, 1980), persistence of life on the continents since Silurian time may imply that, for the last 400 myr, oxygen levels have never fallen below 10% of the present atmospheric level (which is the minimum abundance needed to maintain an effective protective ozone layer). On the maximal end, it seems unlikely that oxygen attained more than twice its present level during these 400 myr, since the flammability of dry organic substances rises rapidly with an increase in oxygen pressure. If oxygen concentration had been very high, land life might have been threatened by catastrophic fires. Neither of these arguments tells us much about conditions prior to 400 myr ago. Berry and Wilde (1978) consider the widespread deposition of black shales in Ordovician and Silurian times to be evidence of low oxygen pressures, lasting until Devonian time. On the other hand, the widespread formation of oxidized marine sediments in early Cambrian time is said to provide evidence of high oxygen pressures at that earlier date (Fischer, 1981).

Two other lines of evidence bear circumstantially on the history of oxygen: the history of carbon isotope ratios in marine carbonate sediments, and that of sulfur isotopes in marine sulfate deposits.

Photosynthesis preferentially removes the lighter isotope, ^{12}C, concentrating it in organic carbon compounds and leaving the CO_2 remaining in the water and the atmosphere enriched in heavier ^{13}C. As light organic carbon accumulates in sedimentary rocks (in the form of kerogen, coal, and petroleum), the average weight of carbon atoms left in carbon dioxide in the atmosphere and dissolved in the ocean shifts toward the heavy side. As a result, the carbon of limestone deposited from the oceans, which is drawn from this CO_2 reservoir, is enriched in the heavier isotope, relative to organic material or sedimentary rocks, by about 25 parts per thousand. The history of carbon isotope values in marine limestones (calcium carbonate formed by nonphotosynthetic reactions), averaged by period, is shown in fig. IV-4. Isotopically speaking, the average weight of the carbon atoms in Cambrian and Ordovician limestones is on the light side. Then, during late Ordovician, Silurian, and early Devonian time (coincident with the colonization of the continents by plants and invertebrates), the isotopic ratio of inorganic carbon in limestones began to shift toward the heavy side, reaching extreme values in the Permian. After this the limestone carbon isotopes decrease in average weight once more, then increase again to reach a secondary heavyweight peak in Cretaceous time, and finally decline in average weight to the modern value. This implies that storage of light organic carbon fixed by photosynthesis (and therefore the cumulative net amount of free oxygen generated and consumed in the organic cycle) peaked in the Permian period, then declined, then peaked again in the Cretaceous period, and declined after that time. The immense volumes of late Carboniferous coal and Cretaceous oil constitute parts of the organic carbon reservoirs established in connection with these events. This cannot be directly translated into a measure of free oxygen in the atmosphere and hydrosphere, however, because other reactions (in particular, the loss of oxygen to the weathering of pyrite) were also involved. For further evidence we turn to the sulfur cycle.

In igneous and metamorphic rocks, sulfur occurs primarily in the form of pyrite, FeS_2. Weathering oxidizes this to ferric oxide (Fe_2O_3) and to sulfate ($SO_4^=$). For every Fe_2O_3 unit formed, four $SO_4^=$ ions are generated. Thus, a major loss of oxygen from the atmosphere is to sulfate. This is mostly added to the dissolved reservoir of sulfate in the oceans, from which it precipitates in two

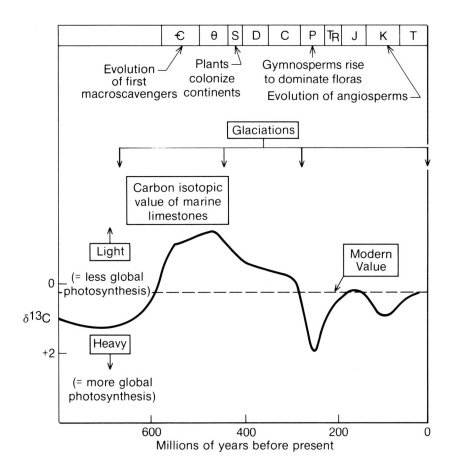

Figure IV-4.— *Change in carbon isotopic values of marine limestones over Phanerozoic time, with inferred relationship to global photosynthesis. (After Veizer et al. (1980).)*

forms, as iron sulfide in bottom muds (caused by the activity of sulfate-reducing bacteria) and as calcium sulfate (gypsum or anhydrite) in evaporite sediments. These reactions produce two sulfur reservoirs in sedimentary rocks: one of *sulfide* and one of *sulfate.*

Sulfur has two common stable isotopes, ^{32}S and ^{34}S (95% and 4.2% of sulfur atoms, respectively). Fractionation of sulfur isotopes occurs in the ocean as a result of supply and withdrawal processes. Even in a very weakly oxidizing atmosphere, sulfur is supplied by weathering as *sulfate,* establishing a dissolved *sulfate reservoir.* The size of this reservoir has no doubt varied considerably through time, as a function of *withdrawals.* These are partly in the form of *sulfate evaporites* (gypsum and anhydrite, precipitated in shallow epicontinental seas of arid regions) and *sulfides* (hydrogen sulfide and pyrite, generated through bacterial action, both in freshly deposited sediments and in stagnant water masses *[sulfureta]* such as the Black Sea today).

Because the bacteria responsible for making sulfide discriminate in favor of the lighter isotope (^{32}S), this is preferentially accumulated in the sulfide reservoir, and the abundance of the light isotope remaining in the seawater is lowered correspondingly. Thus the sulfate remaining in solution, and therefore the sulfate that crystallizes out of it in evaporite settings, has a higher proportion of the heavy isotope (^{34}S) than do bacterially precipitated sulfides. Barring other complications, heavy *sulfate* sulfur isotope ratios imply extensive deposition of sulfide and little deposition of sulfate, and light ratios imply the opposite (Holser and Kaplan, 1966; Garrels and Lerman, 1981).

Sulfate and sulfide deposition varies in intensity through time. Evaporites develop at times when sea levels and continental configurations lead to widespread semilandlocked seas on continents. The extent of sulfide-producing sulfureta seems to have varied greatly, and in response to a variety of factors. The biggest variation over the long run has been that of atmospheric oxygen pressure: the entire ocean was a sulfuretum during the early Precambrian. Its conversion from a sulfidic water mass to the largely oxygenated sulfatic ocean that we know today was a gradual but not monotonic process. What role changing oxygen pressures played in the Phanerozoic variations of the isotope curve remains unknown. Other factors that must have had an effect include the following: (1) whereas oceanic bottom waters today are derived from the cold, highly oxygenated surface waters of the polar regions, it is likely that at times these bottom waters were derived from warm, more saline, less oxygenated waters of the paratropical dry belts; in that case, the extent of sulfureta would have grown. (2) If the rate of oceanic circulation were reduced appreciably, sulfureta would develop widely. (3) If the ocean were to develop more isolated basins and cul-de-sacs, sulfureta would become more common. (4) An increase in the amount of organic matter supplied to the deep waters would also result in a spread of sulfureta.

Such changes undoubtedly affected the isotopic composition of the marine sulfate reservoir as a whole. It is not clear that the evaporite sulfate minerals always reflected that bulk composition: they only record conditions in surface waters. These are now representative of the whole, owing to high mixing rates in the ocean (on the order of a thousand years). There is at least a theoretical possibility that the ocean may at times have seen much less mixing between the deeper water masses (in which sulfureta may develop and which are influenced by sulfate reduction) and the layer of water above the thermocline from which the evaporites are derived. The sharp displacements seen in the sulfur isotope curve (Fig. IV-5; Claypool et al., 1980) are perhaps most readily explained as a result of such differential evolution followed by remixing of the surface and deep reservoirs.

The sulfur isotope curve through Earth history (fig. IV-5) shows that the isotope ratio in sulfate sediments has varied markedly through time. This implies that sulfur was being stored more as sulfate at some times, and more as sulfide at others. The Earth was in a "sulfate mode" in Vendian time (around 650 myr ago) and in Permian and later time. It was in a "sulfide mode" in the early Paleozoic and again in the Tertiary period. In general, the sulfate peaks match the times of oxygen output suggested by the carbon isotope ratios, a relationship that was suggested by Garrels and Perry (1974) and which has since been substantiated by Garrels and Lerman's computer simulation. It is possible, then, that much of the extra oxygen generated during times of maximal storage of organic carbon did not remain in the atmosphere. Rather, it was used up in weathering and was transferred to the lithosphere as sulfate and, to a lesser extent, as ferric iron oxide. How much the atmospheric oxygen pressure actually increased remains conjectural.

An event that suggests changes in atmospheric oxygen pressure is the recurring, widespread establishment of dysoxia or anoxia in an "oxygen minimum" layer of the ocean directly below the thermocline in ancient times (Fischer and Arthur, 1977; Jenkyns, 1980). Such a deficiency of oxygen was so widespread during parts of the Ordovician, Silurian, Devonian, Jurassic, and Cretaceous periods that local factors seem inadequate to explain it.

These occurrences are not necessarily related to changes in atmospheric oxygen levels, however. They could reflect a general decrease in the rate of oceanic circulation, allowing normal rates of organic respiration to draw down the oceanic reservoir of dissolved oxygen to low levels, or an increased organic productivity at the surface, with the consequent creation of so much detritus that the decay of this sinking material overwhelmed the oxygen reserves of the subthermoclinal waters. Whatever the cause, this layer must have interposed a widespread barrier

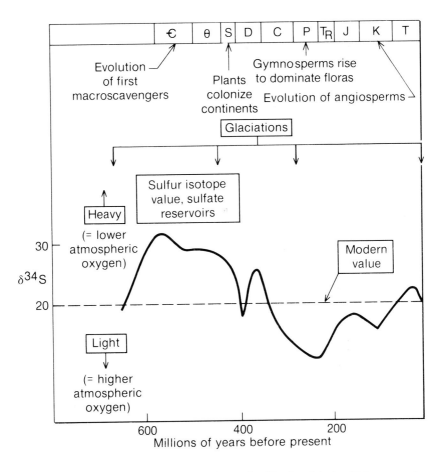

Figure IV-5.— *Change in isotopic values of sulfur in global sulfate reservoirs over Phanerozoic time, with inferred relationship to atmospheric oxygen. (After Claypool et al. (1980).)*

between the deep (bathypelagic) and shoal (epipelagic) faunas at times. Diurnal migration of pelagic organisms, so widespread in the present ocean, may have been interrupted or nonexistent over wide areas. Large parts of the bottoms at intermediate depths became uninhabited at these times.

Although direct measurements are not possible, it is apparent from observations on isotopic ratios of carbon and sulfur and from the history of life (with its evident changes in abundance and the diversity of both photosynthetic and consumer organisms) that atmospheric (and perhaps oceanic) oxygen concentrations have probably fluctuated considerably over the past half billion years. This may have been of importance to the evolution of complex life because of the vital role of oxygen in respiratory physiology. Further means of studying this important factor should be sought.

d. Changes in Atmospheric Carbon Dioxide Levels

Carbon dioxide serves as the source of carbon for all organisms, even though the direct acquisition of carbon from CO_2 is accomplished only by producer organisms. The carbon dioxide cycle is reviewed in various books, including those of Holland (1978), Budyko (1977), and Bolin et al. (1979). Carbon dioxide is transferred from the Earth's mantle and crust to the atmosphere and hydrosphere by volcanism. It returns to the solid Earth, first by conversion to bicarbonate in solution, then by precipitation as carbonate in the hydrosphere. Within this slow cycle runs a much faster one in which carbon is incorporated into the living biomass by photosynthesis, and is returned to the atmosphere-hydrosphere system by the respiration of producer, consumer, and decomposer organisms, and by fire. Reduced carbon is returned to the solid crust in the form of organic matter. Changes in the rates of global volcanism and in the rates of weathering must be reflected by changes of carbon dioxide levels in the atmosphere and hydrosphere (Fischer, 1982).

Most plants investigated thus far operate most efficiently at about three times the present atmospheric carbon dioxide pressure and can tolerate increases of an order of magnitude or more. They cease to function, however, if CO_2 pressure drops to a quarter of its present value. The present terrestrial floras are therefore in the

86

lower part of what we may consider to be their "carbon dioxide stability field."

Analyses of gases from ice formed in the Wisconsin glacial interval suggest that carbon dioxide levels were about 26% lower than the present value during the last ice age (Neftel et al., 1982). This lower level approaches the lower limit of tolerance of higher plants. It is conceivable, therefore, that life on Earth has been limited at times by low availability of atmospheric carbon dioxide.

Higher carbon dioxide levels can influence climates. The transparency of carbon dioxide to the short-wave radiation of the visible spectrum, combined with its opacity to infrared radiation, produces the well-known "greenhouse effect." Manabe and Wetherald (1975) calculated that doubling atmospheric carbon dioxide pressure would raise the global mean annual temperature by several degrees Celsius. This effect would not be globally uniform, but would be much smaller in the tropics (where heat is largely converted into water vapor) and much larger in higher latitudes, where increased rainfall would release much latent energy.

Fischer (1981) suggests that atmospheric carbon dioxide pressure has been significantly influenced by cycles in lithospheric plate activity, which are probably linked to mantle convection. Times of rapid plate motion correspond to times of high sea level and extensive volcanism. At such times, the rate of supply of CO_2 to the hydrosphere and atmosphere from the mantle and crust would be maximal because of volcanism, and removal of CO_2 from the atmosphere would be minimal, partly because of lesser atmospheric contact with the reduced land areas. Conversely, during times of quiescence in plate activity, volcanism would be reduced and the sea level would drop. This would reduce the supply of CO_2 to the fluid envelope of the Earth, and increase the demand for CO_2 by weathering processes because of the greater area of exposed land.

B. RESEARCH RECOMMENDATIONS

The study of the influence of broad-scale environmental change on evolution in the biosphere has never been systematically attempted, either on the scope of worldwide effects or on the time scale equivalent to the Phanerozoic eon (0.6 byr). Four major areas of research are appropriate to NASA's interest in the evolution of complex life on the Earth as an example of what might occur on any similar planet in the Milky Way Galaxy. These are

(1) Patterns of paleogeographic change, associated biogeographic change, and their influences on evolution

(2) Feedback systems between the biosphere and the physical environment that influence evolution or the conditions for evolution

(3) Possible patterns of cyclicity in environmental change

(4) The limits to environmental change (and rates of change) that are tolerable and/or optimal to the evolution of complex life

Recommendation 1: Patterns of Paleogeographic and Biogeographic Change

Although it is now known that the geography of the Earth has changed continuously throughout the Phanerozoic eon and that this change has repeatedly isolated biogeographic regions and then brought them back into contact, we do not know the actual evolutionary impacts of this change except in a few instances. Documentation of the relation between geographic changes through time and changes in regional biotas would allow tests of many aspects of general evolutionary theory and would permit the development of new theory to apply at the planetary level.

There are two ways in which the effects of continental movement on the evolution and diversity of life can be studied. First, detailed analysis of the fossil record that remains on each of the major tectonic plates can be undertaken. This sort of study, conducted by Simpson (1960) and others, revealed the pattern of vertebrate extinction (and insights on the relative adaptive fitnesses of animals of different design) that accompanied the late Pliocene encounter between the previously isolated faunas of North and South America. Second, systematic work on groups of living organisms that are known to be relatively old and widespread can be encouraged. These include families and orders whose fossil records can be traced to early Mesozoic time, or earlier. Here, the goal should be a recapitulation of the phylogeny of each "old" group. One advantage of this systematic approach is that data from both living and fossil members of each group can be used to compile an account of its evolutionary history. Once compiled, these data can provide insights into paleobiogeographic distributions and, perhaps, reasons for the "successes" of these groups at avoiding extinction.

At this time, realistic paleogeographies are still being compiled. Thanks to the prospect of finding synchronous benchmarks in geological strata, left there by extraterrestrial events of the past (see Recommendation 5, chapter III), it may be possible to delineate the distributions of ancient plants and animals with an exactitude that has never been attainable in the past. Once the histories of "old" taxonomic groups, the patterns of ancient geographies, and the distributions of ancient organisms become better known, new clues to the emergence (and extinction) of complex life of the past will be forthcoming. No thorough review of paleobiogeography within the context of realistic paleogeography has ever been attempted. We recommend that such an effort be made.

Recommendation 2: Feedback Between Living Systems and the Physical Environment

Biological activity has had a profound effect upon the composition of the atmosphere. Estimates of the extents of the changes wrought by organisms, and of their impacts upon the physical environment and upon life itself, are still highly speculative. Typical questions are, "How much oxygen was present when multicellular eukaryotes were beginning to evolve?" "Has the evolution of plants altered atmospheric CO_2 levels sufficiently to have altered world climates?" "Might an evolutionary radiation of plants create glacial polar climates (for example, by an increase of photosynthetic activity, a reduction of atmospheric CO_2 levels, and an elimination of greenhouse conditions)?" "How have atmospheric changes and direct contributions of organic molecules to the Earth's surface influenced the rates of weathering and control of soil chemistry?"

The tightest feedback between organisms and physical-chemical environments envisioned at present is that embodied in Lovelock's GAIA hypothesis (Lovelock, 1979). In his view, biological activities not only dominate the surface chemistry of the

Earth, but organisms also evolve in ways that ultimately allow them to maintain the suitability of global climates and surface conditions, and in ways that cause them to resist climatic departures from that range of general suitability. An alternative and more commonly accepted view acknowledges the significant effects of living organisms on global chemistry without accepting the premise that evolution endows organisms with an improved ability to keep surface conditions favorable for themselves. As the contributions of nonliving processes such as volcanism and continental drift become better recognized, a new view favoring the increased significance of purely inorganic controls of environmental suitability for life is not inconceivable. It is clear that some of the most significant questions about the relationships between complex life and the habitability of the Earth (as well as that of other planets) lie in this area. The relative importances of nonliving and life processes in establishing and maintaining global habitability, and the particular question of whether organisms evolve toward improved capability of doing so, deserve further study. We recommend that these questions be pursued in an effort to learn the degree to which complex life is capable of maintaining suitable environmental conditions for itself, and its ability to retard (or prevent) adverse climatic and other changes in the environments of the planet upon which it occurs.

Recommendation 3: Possible Patterns of Cyclicity in Environmental Change

There appears to be a Phanerozoic "bimodality" in many environmental factors, including climate, atmospheric composition, and paleogeography. Late Proterozoic, late Ordovician, late Paleozoic, and recent times experienced glaciation, low sea levels, and clustered continents. The early Paleozoic and late Mesozoic eras were times of warmer climates, dispersed continents, and high sea levels. These and other factors may all relate to a general pattern of internal Earth dynamics (perhaps a pattern of convection in the mantle), or they may be independent and simply coincidental. Whereas some may result from internal Earth dynamics, others may result from fluctuations in solar radiation, encounters of the solar system with clouds of galactic dust during its orbit of the galaxy, or other Space-related effects. There are also many short-term environmental fluctuations, ranging in duration from that of the advances and retreats of continental ice sheets (on a scale of 10^5 yr) to diurnal phenomena. All of these must affect the evolution of life. The sedimentary record contains features such as rhythmic bedding that reveal such cycles (Schwarzacher and Fischer, 1982). The impacts of these "pulses in nature" on the course of evolution should be investigated. Can true cyclicities be unambiguously documented? What are the influences of various cycles on the biosphere? Investigation of such questions could help to assess the possible influences of environmental patterns on other planets on the evolution of their complex organisms.

Recommendation 4: The Limits of Environmental Change Tolerable to Complex Life

Extreme and rapid changes in environmental conditions can exceed the tolerance of living systems and destroy them. Yet a certain rate of disturbance, perhaps coupled with extinctions and providing new opportunities for speciation, may create conditions in which evolution can proceed more rapidly. What are the optimal conditions for accelerating evolution? How has the Earth avoided environmental perturbations so extreme as to eliminate all life? Are conditions that stimulate and drive evolution, comparable to those found on Earth, common elsewhere in the universe? Is the lack of extreme perturbations that has characterized the Earth common elsewhere? Answers to these questions are vital to a better understanding of the development of life on Earth and to an understanding of the potential for the evolution of complex life in other planetary environments.

CHAPTER V
EVOLUTIONARY PROCESSES

D. H. Milne, K. J. Niklas, and K. Padian

A. INTRODUCTION

Chapter IV has emphasized that many changes have occurred on the surface of the Earth during the last 1 byr of its history. Continents have collided and separated, ice ages have waxed and waned, seas have advanced and retreated, and events in the solar system and space beyond have modulated the input of sunlight, peppered the surface with meteorites and radiation, and altered the rhythms of the tides. Chapter III has illustrated the ways in which living organisms have changed in their appearances, their diversity, their anatomical complexity, and the complexity of their relationships with the environment (and each other) during the time in which these environmental disturbances have occurred. In the present chapter, we relate the preceding chapters by exploring some of the processes by which changes in the complexity of living organisms are related to, or prompted by, changes in their environments.

The "environment" of an organism includes its physical setting and the other organisms around it. The effects of both physical and biotic components must be considered if the mechanisms of evolution are to be understood. Understanding biological evolution also depends upon knowing the general properties of living organisms. The ways in which they are able to change, and the rates at which change is made possible, depend heavily upon built-in constraints that may or may not be unique to terrestrial life. The rates at which organisms are able to grow and reproduce (which in turn depend upon details of their genetics, biochemistry, and physiology), the ways in which their genomes are capable of being modified and transmitted to other generations, and other details of their construction all influence the rates and types of change that they are able to experience.

In addition to accounting for the effects of environments and properties of organisms, our understanding of evolution must be based upon knowledge of the ways in which the potential for change in organisms is actually realized. Why should a population of organisms that has persisted relatively unchanged for several million years "suddenly" begin to transform itself into some other species? What do organisms have to do, or what sorts of situations must arise, in order to activate the subtle interplay of environmental prompting and genetic response that, continued over many generations, gives rise to new life forms? In this chapter we ask, therefore, *how evolution works:* what processes make it go. These questions build upon the knowledge developed in chapters III and IV; their answers may better explain the pattern of development of complex life on the Earth — and perhaps elsewhere.

B. THE GENETIC BASIS OF COMPLEX LIFE

"Simple" organisms — bacteria and other prokaryotes — usually owe their shapes and biochemical abilities to a coded molecular "message" that is composed of a single DNA molecule. Each cell contains one such molecule. "Complex" organisms usually contain the equivalent of two complete messages in each cell. The structures that carry these DNA messages are called "chromosomes." The chromosomes are housed in a subcellular package, the nucleus. An organism whose cells contain two complete DNA messages is said to be "diploid"; one whose chromosomes are contained in a nucleus is said to be "eukaryotic." Both conditions seem to represent major mileposts that single-celled organisms needed to pass in order to advance to multicellularity and higher complexities. The study of the origin of diploidy, the eukaryotic condition, and multicellularity is central to any under-standing of the further evolution of complex life. At present, the relationship between these three conditions is not well understood.

Evolutionary change in organisms begins with changes in their coded molecular messages. Changes can occur in single nucleo-tides, in genes, or in whole chromosomes. These changes, called "mutations," are caused by agents such as radiation or mutagenic chemicals, or they may occur spontaneously. Some mutations cause detrimental changes, others seem to cause no change, and a few confer immediate benefit. Statistically speaking, those that cause beneficial changes will tend to be preserved and to accumu-late, as the organisms that bear them tend to produce more viable offspring than those that don't. The occurrence of mutation, therefore, maintains a certain low level of random experimenta-tion with the details of organic designs. Although a great deal of evolution can occur without the appearance of any new mutations at all, they provide the only known feedstock of new genetic material, without which evolution would eventually grind to a halt.

In sexually reproducing organisms, variation also results from recombination of existing genetic information. This occurs during gamete formation in reproduction and has the effect of placing a shuffled version of the genetic material of two parent organisms in each of their offspring. The number of possible combinations is nearly infinite, and the process provides a pool of variation that serves as raw material for evolution.

C. EVOLUTIONARY PROCESSES AND THEIR OUTCOMES

1. Natural Selection

Natural selection was first described in convincing terms by Charles Darwin (1859); much of his description of the process is still valid today. As he saw it, natural selection is a consequence of the following phenomena:

95

(a) All organisms differ from each other; as a consequence, some are better adapted to prevailing environmental conditions than are others of the same species

(b) All organisms produce more offspring than their environment can support; as a consequence, only a few members of each new generation survive and reproduce.

Favorable genetic information conferring "fitness" or adaptation is thereby "naturally selected" in a manner that is analogous to the deliberate selection, by a human breeder, of traits in plants and animals that are agriculturally desirable. It is here that new and desirable improvements — small random increases in anatomical or behavioral complexity, improvements in metabolic function and the like, resulting from mutation or fortuitous chromosome recombinations — are "caught" and retained by living systems. It is here that the random processes that generate changes in organisms, be they harmful, neutral, or beneficial, encounter nonrandom forces that sift the alternatives and systematically retain the ones that have survival value. The process is not an infallible one, nor is it infinitely sensitive. An organism with a very small new advantage may not be "noticed" by the selective forces in nature, simply because it never finds itself in a situation in which that small improvement makes a practical difference, or because that barely discernible improvement fails to make an impression the first time it occurs. This situation is almost always complicated by the fact that genetic changes seldom influence just one property of an organism.

Modern evolutionary thought distinguishes between "stabilizing selection" and "directional selection" (for example, see Mayr, 1963; Simpson, 1953). The former is commonly regarded as characteristic of relatively stable environments and is summarized by the statement, "if the environment doesn't change, then neither will the organisms." In stabilizing selection, individuals that deviate too greatly from some average structure or morphology (which is adapted to the stable environment) are selected against. This process may account, in part, for the fact that many fossil lineages show little or no change over periods of millions of years.

The counterpart of this argument ("directional selection"), for organisms in environments in which change is unidirectional and slow enough to permit the evolution of successive generations to keep up with it, suggests a scenario by which certain gradual changes, seen in some fossil lineages, may have occurred. Both arguments have loopholes, however. Organisms have such potential for rapid divergence from the phenotypes of their ancestors, and environments are so unlikely to remain precisely stable over millions of years that "stabilizing selection" may have hitherto unexplained ramifications and dimensions. Similarly, not all of the change seen in the fossil record is gradual. Certain changes, perhaps, may be too abrupt to be explained as ordinary selectional responses to slow unidirectional environmental change. And situations can be envisioned in which nonchanging environments might permit directional change, and changing environments might inhibit certain evolutionary trends, in certain lineages. Exciting new hypotheses about evolution are, in fact, emerging from current careful analyses of the possible relationships between environmental change (or lack of change) and directional and stabilizing selection.

The diversity of selective environmental factors, the mechanisms of mutation, and the mode of gene recombination in bisexual reproduction ensure that genetic change from generation to generation is complex and random in several important ways. The fates of individuals, or the outcomes of evolution in single specific instances, cannot be predicted in systems characterized by such complexity, compounded by partially random occurrences. Average trends, however, and certain other aspects of evolution, can be ascertained via statistical or stochastic modeling. We cannot speak confidently about exact directions in which evolution will proceed. We can, however, describe and consider the relative importances of certain evolutionary factors in particular situations, and formulate with some assurance, general expectations as to their effects.

2. Adaptive Responses to Natural Selection

The tendency of environmental factors to discriminate against the least fit individuals results in the continued maintenance of overall fitness of each species, and a shift in fitness parameters as the environment changes through time. The shift in fitness may take the form of appropriate behavior, protective coloration, biochemical abilities, ecological specialization or generalization, structural change, or combinations of these features. Effective morphological, physiological, and behavioral strategies for coping with environmental factors (which may be constant or intermittent) are termed "adaptations."

There is more than one way for an organism to adapt to the demands of the environment. A given species may be faced with a variety of different environments, or environmental factors, with which it must successfully deal in order to survive. Within that species, there may be many genetically distinct forms (genotypes), each potentially adapted to a different set of environmental factors that is likely to be encountered, but none potentially suitable for all environmental situations. An alternative solution is possession of one "all-purpose" genotype that creates a form plastic enough to respond to the whole anticipated range of environmental conditions. In reality, both solutions are used by all organisms. The two alternatives are not mutually exclusive, but are synergistic.

The adaptive responses of various species are often correlated with the types of environments they inhabit. For example, populations living in relatively uncertain environments often reproduce sooner and more frequently than do those living in relatively stable environments (MacArthur and Wilson, 1967). Individuals in such situations tend to be shorter-lived and to produce many offspring, each of which has a small overall probability of survival. This is a "numbers game," played with many propagules and small chances of individual survival. Certain groups use an alternative strategy: they maximize the efficiency and success of reproduction and individual survival. Many green plants have adopted this alternative strategy, producing propagules that are dormant and that germinate only under favorable conditions. These reproductive modes are of considerable importance in assessing the alternative possibilities of evolutionary success in changing environments. Each reproductive strategy is particularly viable under certain environmental conditions. We are not sure that the environment has forced these strategies on the various types of organisms, but it is apparent that these strategies are explicitly adaptive for the environments inhabited by the organisms. Other adaptive strategies similarly provide clues to the nature of environmental stresses, and to ways in which organisms can change to cope with them.

D. THE FORMATION AND EXTINCTION OF SPECIES

Chapter II outlines some ways in which an existing species can give rise to one or more new species. Some of the environmental dimensions of this process are well understood. For example, we recognize that organisms of a single species, dispersed into regions that are isolated from each other by geographical barriers, will often give rise to new species (Mayr, 1963). Many questions remain, however, particularly with regard to the potential for speciation in regions that are only partially isolated, or ones that are broadly confluent. We are not certain about the exact relationship between geographic complexity and species diversity; the relationship between geography and genetics also requires further analysis (Templeton, 1981).

The genetic attributes that favor speciation are not well understood. This knowledge appears to be needed for assessing the degrees to which organisms can potentially evolve and, perhaps, for understanding the mechanisms involved in the timing of speciation with respect to other biologic and environmental change. The genetic attributes of certain organisms may be particularly revealing in this context. For example, some lineages of animals and plants are more speciose than others. Can we address the issue of why these organisms seem to be more capable of speciation, and therefore more likely to produce a diversity of types that would favor survival in changing conditions? Genetic, ecological, and distributional mechanisms have been proposed to account for differences between very speciose and depauperate taxonomic groups (Stanley, 1979). The genetic variations considered include karyotypic variation, enzyme polymorphism, and the plasticity of regulatory genes. Genetic attributes of other organisms, or of organisms in unique environmental situations, may reveal equally valuable insights into the basis of speciation.

Currently, our knowledge of the correlation between genetic variability and taxonomic and morphologic diversity is insufficient, but data now obtainable could allow an extensive survey of these relationships by the integration of biochemical, morphologic, and paleontologic lines of evidence. Because many of these data are already available, their synthesis can be undertaken with relative ease and efficiency and used to determine approximate correspondences among the comparative complexities of the various hierarchical levels of evolution.

It is clear that environmental factors (geographical complexity and disturbance frequency, among others) play a critical role in filtering genetic variants. Extrinsic environmental factors such as physical heterogeneity and temporal instability can be measured on global or intercontinental bases. These measurements of the environment could be compared and correlated with the apparent "speciosity" of taxa in discrete environments. Such analyses might provide an empirical basis for determining conditions that favor rapid evolution.

It is natural to think of extinction as the counterpoint to speciation, the process that balances the addition of species to the biosphere by inexorably and inevitably removing them. As noted in chapter II, extinction may be viewed as a background process that is constantly at work, independent of speciation, with an ever-present potential to eventually terminate all terrestrial life. Certain processes that "drive" extinction are far beyond the control of living organisms, and may qualify as independent background threats to much of life.

Chapters II and III have noted the potential significance of extinction to the progressive development of complexity in some of the Earth's living things. In some cases (although this is not proven, and is indeed disputed), the extinction of certain organisms may "liberate" others, providing them with new opportunities in the recently vacated landscape in which they find themselves. The great extinction of dinosaurs during the final part of the Cretaceous Period was followed by an evolutionary radiation of mammals. The physical and floral environments of terrestrial vertebrates were so changeable at that time that testing the question of "liberation" may be extremely difficult. However, it is quite possible that extinction may ironically "promote" the evolution of new and perhaps different complexity in this rather oblique way. It is clear that extinction also reduces biotic complexity at times, however, especially that of communities. The mammal fauna of the modern Earth is far less diverse today than it was at the beginning of the Pleistocene epoch, as a result of the selective global extinctions of large mammals that occurred before about 6000 BC (Martin and Wright, 1967).

Extinction usually seems to be caused by changes in the physical and biological environments. In instances where change is staggering and instantaneous (as, for example, that which might accompany a volcanic eruption or asteroid impact at ground zero), it is obvious why the affected species are eradicated. In cases in which environmental change is slow and subtle, however, the causes of extinction become more difficult to document. There may be many different causes applicable to different instances. Here, the careful study of selected living communities (which, unfortunately, are severely affected by the direct and indirect effects of human activities) can reveal many of the details of mechanisms that might have contributed to extinctions of the past and which are currently not well understood.

The reduction of the number of individuals of a species by habitat destruction, excessive predation, or other means seems to be a first (but reversible) step in the extinction process. Environmental changes, including deterioration of the physical environment and increasing competition from other species (particularly recent invaders) probably play a role in the initial reductions in numbers of individuals of a species. As population size decreases, other processes are set in motion. Difficulty in finding mates, loss of genetic potential for future change, continued loss of genetic variability via accelerated random drift, and the risk of mortality from minor local environmental reverses, compounded by whatever difficult conditions are responsible for reducing a population's size in the first place, may eventually drive a species past the "point of no return," beyond which its demise is relatively swift and certain.

The activities of organisms, and particularly the processes of speciation, may also contribute to the mechanisms of extinction. As new organisms continually appear on the scene, either by evolution *in situ* or by arrival from isolated regions in which they arose, they themselves constitute a change in the environments of the indigenous organisms. Several episodes of extinction in Earth history have apparently been instigated by confrontations of organisms of different taxa. Most notable was the disappearance of many North and South American mammals shortly after their continental homelands became connected by the Panamanian land bridge. At that time, mammals that had evolved in isolation from each other moved from each continent into the other, and many whole families became extinct within a few million years.

In order to understand the development of complexity in organisms, we must more clearly define the relationship (if any) between speciation and extinction, and determine as exactly as is possible the mechanisms by which species become extinct under ordinary noncatastrophic circumstances, as well as in extraordinary or catastrophic situations.

E. CURRENT FRONTIERS OF EVOLUTIONARY THEORY

Evolutionary theory is currently in the midst of a critical review that is as profound as any that has occurred in the entire history of evolutionary thought. Emerging from this reevaluation are new views of processes and phenomena that can significantly alter our understanding of the evolution of complex life on the Earth, and of its possible occurrence elsewhere in the universe. Among others, the following significant questions are currently under discussion:

(1) Does morphologic evolution usually proceed at a constant steady pace? Or does it usually proceed by erratic fits and starts?

(2) Why do species have so much genetic variation (commonly affecting 30% or more of their genes) and how much of this variation is related to standard evolutionary processes, including natural selection?

(3) Are small genetic changes continued for long periods sufficient to explain all of the major changes that have occurred throughout the history of life? Or have other (perhaps more rarely occurring) modes of change also contributed to those evolutionary developments?

(4) Can some evolutionary change be explained by processes other than natural selection? In particular, can random changes in

the genetic makeup of successive generations impose directionalities that are independent of, or even contrary to, those that straightforward selection would produce?

(5) To what extent does natural selection operate on levels above that of the individual organism? Are kin groups, local populations, or even whole species selected in some manner that is analogous to the selection of individual organisms?

Questions (1) and (2) relate to a concept that has been termed "Punctuated Equilibria." This view considers that the persistence of fossil species in relatively unchanged morphology over long periods of geological time, followed by their abrupt disappearance and replacement by others that are noticeably different and that seem to have evolved from them, accurately reflects the tempo and mode of evolution, rather than irregularities in the pattern of geological deposition and preservation. In this view, morphological change often proceeds by occasional, relatively rapid advances that alternate with long periods of "stasis" (that is, little evolutionary change). The stasis interval is dominant, being "punctuated" by relatively short intervals of morphologic change which, though perhaps long in terms of years, are sufficiently short not to have been preserved in the geologic record. This view is a significant departure from the traditional view that most morphologic change (though not all) is relatively slow and steady, proceeding within the life span of the species (rather than during the brief period during which the species originates). The Punctuated Equilibria concept is developed in detail by Eldredge and Gould (1972); a critique is presented by Grant (1982).

In practice, the question of Punctuated Equilibria has several important ramifications for the evolution of complexity. First is the basic observation of Punctuated Equilibria: that *stasis* in most morphologic features is the rule, not the exception, in the fossil record. What maintains this stasis, and how can it be maintained for so long? An easy answer is "stabilizing selection," but if that is the reason, then one must accept either that the environment almost never changes, or that a sufficiently buffered all-purpose phenotype (canalized, perhaps, by developmental constraints) comes with an evolutionary "warranty" that is good for periods of up to 10 or 15 myr!

A second problem relates to the identification of the processes and the relative time spans involved in the transformation from one "stable" form to another. Obviously the transformation is not an overnight phenomenon. However, its temporal limits are unclear. It must occur over many biological generations, but even though these may span tens (or hundreds) of thousands of years, an event of this duration occurs so instantaneously, in a geologic sense, that it may leave no preserved record at all.

A third problem relates to the genetic mechanisms that underlie such morphologic change. Is the nature of the variation, and the type of change recorded, identifiable with the sorts of variations and changes seen in modern populations? What sorts of genetic systems are most likely to be affected by rapid, consequential change, and what factors instigate the change?

Finally, does the change from one morphologic state to another imply that a new adaptation has been gained, that an old one has been lost, or that both may still be expressed in future circumstances? The understanding of these and other problems is of primary value to the realization of how biological complexity is evolved, maintained, and increased.

F. RESEARCH RECOMMENDATIONS

Recommendation 1: Organism-Environment Interactions and the Evolution of Complexity

The long haul of geologic time reveals a phenomenon that is not likely to be seen in modern studies of speciation. This is the appearance of "evolutionary innovation" or "adaptive breakthrough." Evolutionary innovations appear to foster bursts of species diversity, adaptive radiations, and the filling of adaptive zones with the ecological niches of individual species. The pattern of explosive bursts of speciation and radiation, following close on the heels of each adaptive breakthrough, is well documented in the fossil record. Indeed, the major taxonomic groups, which correspond roughly to evolutionary units reflecting particular adaptive breakthroughs (e.g., Van Valen, 1971), show a consistent pattern

104

of rapid diversification within the first 25% of their geologic history, then an equally rapid decrease to a more-or-less stable level of diversity that is rarely affected by another pronounced evolutionary burst (Thomson, 1976). These observations suggest that an adaptive breakthrough, which may be characterized as a significant ecological, morphological, or adaptational reorganization of species, in effect generates two hierarchical levels of evolution: morphologic complexity and species diversity. Such innovations effectively define "complex and higher organisms"; their study should be of central importance to NASA.

The following questions are raised by the study of the evolution of complex adaptations:

(1) What patterns can be seen in the relationship between the environment of a taxon and its subsequent adaptive breakthrough?

(2) Are there indications that the environment fosters such change, and if so, are the factors that do so mainly biotic or abiotic?

(3) What various kinds of complexity arise during the course of the evolution of adaptation?

(4) Is there evidence that achievement of certain kinds of complexity is more or less probable?

(5) Are there discernible trends in the development of evolutionary complexity, and can such patterns shed light on the evolutionary process?

The principal means of studying complex adaptations is to elucidate their patterns, using evidence from comparative biology and paleontology (see also chapter III). Phylogenetic analysis of evolutionary patterns is a rigorous inexpensive means of laying bare the historical sequence of adaptive progression (Eldredge and Cracraft, 1980; Lauder, 1981). The evolution of adaptive function can be tested independently, often using experimental models that simulate natural factors and provide a baseline of data for assessing the efficiency or workability of an adaptation. Much of the technology that could be applied to the study of adaptation (for example, the gliding and flight abilities of birds and mammals) includes stress-testing equipment, experimental monitors of many kinds, and wind tunnels of the sort that are already part of NASA's working stock in trade. Other major adaptations that could be investigated under the aegis of this project include feeding and sensory innovations, structural breakthroughs, and environmental manipulation. Examples include the evolution of adaptations for living and moving on land, movement with a hydraulic skeleton, high-speed swimming, and intelligence. An understanding of the biologic and environmental contributors to adaptive breakthrough is fundamental to Project ECHO because these innovations are most likely to result in organisms that are progressively more capable of responding flexibly to their environment and controlling it to some degree. We need a better systematic understanding of the evolutionary processes leading to complex adaptation. This is, after all, one of the basic properties of complex life, and human intelligence is a noteworthy example.

Recommendation 2: Physical *a Priori* Nature of Life Forms

Although paleontology and genetics may tell us about the tempo and mode of evolutionary change, they do not establish physical and mechanical limits to life as we know it. All living forms must develop and function in conformity to physical laws. An effort should be made to identify the *a priori* constraints on biologic form that must have limited the possibilities for life on Earth. On this basis we may assess the extent to which those limits would hold for other planetary systems in the universe.

The understanding of design in organisms has led to investigations of the relative efficiency or optimality of certain designs in given environmental conditions. The principles of natural selection suggest that, at the organismal level at least, evolution should act to optimize survival value and, by inference, adaptiveness. This does not imply that each of the particular parts of organisms is optimized, but it is reasonable to suggest that the limits of certain structural properties may predict greater survival value or, alternately, greater probability of extinction for organisms that rely upon certain kinds of biologic materials to solve the problems of existence. The abilities of various body forms *(Baupläne)* to respond to changes in the environment may be predictable, given knowledge of the limits of the mechanical properties of biological materials.

On Earth, many biological materials are used to give living things their familiar forms. Some materials (such as cellulose) are more commonly used than are others (such as strontium sulphate), and structural possibilities that are wholly unknown on Earth may be more feasible or more common elsewhere. Experimental investigations of this question could include analyses of stress-strain properties of biological materials such as bone, chitin, silica, lignin, and cellulose, and determination of the environmental conditions (including gravitational forces) under which they can be developed by organisms for solving problems of design and function. For complex organisms, it is also useful to investigate the influence of mechanical stress on the organization, interaction, and differentiation of biological tissues, and the compressive and tensile properties of relevant biologic materials under different conditions of stress (see, for example, Niklas and O'Rourke, 1982). Extrapolation of this understanding to other possible planetary environments would provide insights into the limitations of certain forms and their evolution in such environments.

Recommendation 3: Environmental Limits to Life

The Paleozoic Era saw the invasion and colonization of new and relatively benign habitats (deep mud, the pelagic realm, and the continents) by complex organisms (fig. III-5). As a part of that trend, organisms have also invaded and colonized more rigorous environments, including deserts, the Antarctic continent, and the thermal vents of the deep sea. The living things that have successfully invaded these stressful habitats have become adapted to some of the most severe physical conditions on Earth. They indicate the limits of pressure, temperature, duration of daylight, and other factors that complex organisms of terrestrial biochemistries and morphologies are able to tolerate. We recommend that the mechanisms of tolerance to these environmental extremes be studied in selected taxa, in order to establish

(1) Absolute and impenetrable environmental limits to the existence of complex life on Earth

(2) General parameters of morphologic, physiologic, and behavioral adaptations by which terrestrial life accommodates itself to these extremes

(3) Insights into possible environmental limits on the distribution of complex life, as we know it, elsewhere in the universe

Recommendation 4: Evolutionary Stasis

The relationships among extinction, speciation, and environmental change have been mentioned in previous sections. It is not clear whether mass extinctions, major radiations, and other evolutionary phenomena would occur in the absence of major environmental changes or disturbances. We have noted that speciation and extinction may continue under conditions of environmental stability. Species diversity may well increase indefinitely or decrease to zero, even in very stable environments. Studies of islands and continents, on the other hand, often reveal definite area/diversity relationships — evidence that there are limits to species "packing." However, many factors of this equation, such as age of the associations, energy resources, and trophic structures are not fully understood (see Whittaker, 1977).

Episodes of "stasis" in Earth history have been marked by the apparent cessation of morphological change in certain organisms. However, in living communities that have experienced little apparent change in their physical-chemical environment over many millions of years, speciation continues at a rapid rate. It should be possible, by studies of ecological theory, biogeography, the fossil record and other subjects, to establish whether or not major evolutionary innovation is possible in a "stasis situation" and whether or not occasional mass extinctions are to be expected even in the absence of a major disturbance of the physical environment. We recommend that such studies be pursued.

Recommendation 5: Evolution of Neurophysiological Complexity

The increasing sophistication of the central nervous systems of the animals of recent geological time is clearly an important manifestation of an increase in the complexity of the terrestrial biota.

The definition of neurophysiological complexity is itself an extraordinarily difficult problem. The number and structural complexity of the cellular units and their aggregate mass must be considered, as well as their structural interrelationships ("wiring")

and the number and interrelationships of specialized multicellular substructures within the central nervous system. In addition, the evolution of brain size in relation to body mass should be thoroughly explored. When measures of neurophysiological complexity are better defined, they should be compared to measures of behavioral complexity (some of which may, themselves, require better definition) in order to understand the evolution of the central nervous system in the context of processes of natural selection. Neurophysiological complexity should also be reviewed in historical and biogeographical perspective to determine whether certain environments and ages have been more favorable to its development.

A deeper appreciation of these factors will facilitate an understanding of the implications of data in the fossil record pertaining to levels of organization of central nervous systems in the past. This, in turn, will shed light on trends in neurophysiological evolution, and the probabilities surrounding the subsequent appearance of intelligence, cultural evolution, and science and technological civilizations in the terrestrial biosphere.

CHAPTER VI

EFFECTS OF EXTRATERRESTRIAL PHENOMENA ON THE EVOLUTION OF COMPLEX LIFE ON EARTH

W. H. Berger, J. A. Eddy, and E. M. Shoemaker

A. INTRODUCTION

Broadly speaking, extraterrestrial phenomena that are capable of influencing the evolution of life on Earth fall into four categories. These are

(1) Impingement on the Earth's surface of matter from interplanetary space or from the outer solar system (dust, meteorites, comet nuclei, etc.)

(2) "Initial conditions"; properties of the Earth and Moon, and of their orbits, that were acquired at the time of their formation

(3) Changes in solar radiation incident on the Earth's surface, resulting from changes in the Sun

(4) Radiation and other disturbing factors originating outside the solar system (for example, from supernova explosions)

The phenomena thus categorized produce a variety of different effects at the surface of the Earth. These effects can be conveniently grouped under the headings "Background," "Modulated Effects," and "Unique Events."

Background phenomena are those that are always present, at "strengths" or "intensities" that have remained relatively invariant throughout large fractions (or all) of Earth history. Their effects on the evolution of complex life are difficult to discern. An example of a background factor that has been characteristic of terrestrial environments since the formation of the Earth is the gravitational field. Comparisons of the massive proportions of large land plants and animals with the relatively graceful features of small ones make it clear that gravity imposes definite constraints on the forms that organisms are able to assume. One relatively straightforward way of quantifying and elucidating the constraining role of gravity on evolution would be to compare the forms and evolutionary histories of organisms from regions of different gravitational strengths (and otherwise similar environmental conditions). Since the force of gravity is essentially the same everywhere on the Earth's surface, however, this approach is not possible, at least by simple comparisons of continental organisms. Some insights might be gained by examining aquatic organisms, for which the force of gravity is essentially neutralized by buoyant forces, but such comparisons are complicated by the thousand-fold difference in the densities of air and water, and by other differences between aerial and aquatic environments. This difficulty is characteristic of most efforts to assess and isolate the evolutionary effects and significance of background phenomena. There is a general absence of "controls," of evolutionary experiments conducted in otherwise similar environments in which the background factor is different or lacking.

This is not to say that background phenomena are unimportant in evolution. For example, all ionizing radiation is mutagenic. Cosmic radiation and cosmic-ray-induced radiation must influence rates of alteration of DNA as well as efficiencies of organismic defenses (that is, DNA repair). We may speculate that evolutionary rates are influenced by levels of background cosmic (and other) radiation, therefore, but observational support for such speculation would require a demonstration of differences in evolutionary rates, either before and after a change in background levels, or in separate regions where background levels were not the same. The variation in cosmic ray background with time is not well understood, however, and levels at different sites on the Earth's surface differ by less than one order of magnitude. Temporal changes or regional differences in levels of other background phenomena would also be required to permit the study of their effects; in many cases the necessary changes or differences cannot be identified, or do not exist.

Modulated effects are those that vary periodically in intensity. One important category of modulated effects includes those that cause changes in the pattern of solar irradiation of the Earth's surface. Orbital and galactic mechanisms causing modulation of sunlight have been proposed. Processes within the Sun modulate its radiative output and the cosmic ray flux (via variations in the solar wind magnetic field) as well.

Unique events include occasional short-lived but energetic bombardments of the Earth by asteroids, comets, and heavy fluxes of cosmic rays generated in supernova explosions.

The four categories of extraterrestrial phenomena listed on page 111, and their possible contributions to background, modulated, and unique effects on evolution, are discussed here. A comparative assessment of their potentials as areas for research concludes this section, and is followed by specific research recommendations.

B. EXTRATERRESTRIAL PHENOMENA WITH POTENTIAL FOR INFLUENCING BIOLOGICAL EVOLUTION

1. Comet and Asteroid Impacts on the Earth

Two classes of solid bodies that are large enough to be detected by telescopes occur in orbits that overlap the orbit of the Earth. These bodies are comet nuclei and Earth-crossing asteroids. Their orbits only rarely intersect that of the Earth, but the probabilities of collision are finite and calculable. The estimated present flux of comet nuclei and asteroids in the Earth's neighborhood is roughly consistent with the geological record of Phanerozoic impact structures. During Phanerozoic time the average production rate of impact craters larger than 10 km in diameter was about 2×10^{-14} km^{-2} yr^{-1} (Shoemaker, 1977; Grieve and Dence, 1979).

a. Comets

More than 10^{12} comet nuclei are estimated to occur in a spherical cloud, more than a light year in diameter, that surrounds the solar system. Repeated perturbation of this cloud of comets by passing stars produces a small but fairly steady flux of comets into the region of the planets. Most comets arrive in the Earth's neighborhood on extremely eccentric orbits with periods ranging from thousands to millions of years. Many of these comets are accelerated, by the gravitational attraction of the giant planets, into trajectories that allow them to escape from the solar system. Successive perturbations by the giant planets also result in the transformation of about 0.01% of the long-period comets into comets with short periods (less than 20 yr). About 500 long-period comets have been observed over the past few centuries. Most of these passed inside the orbit of the Earth. Somewhat more than 100 short-period comets have been discovered, but only a small fraction of these cross the Earth's orbit.

Our information about the physical characteristics of comet nuclei is derived chiefly from observation of gases and entrained dust that are liberated as the comets approach the Sun. The nuclei are rotating solid bodies composed chiefly of H_2O ice and embedded rocky particles. An extended dusty atmosphere produced by insolation generally obscures the nucleus of the comet when it is close enough to the Earth for detailed photometric and radiometric observation. For this reason, present estimates of the sizes of comet nuclei are very uncertain. Observations of the amounts of gas and dust released, the acceleration of the comets by the jet-effect of the released material, and direct photometric observations of comet nuclei when they are relatively distant from the Sun suggest that the nuclei range in diameter from less than 1 km to several tens of kilometers.

Shoemaker (1981) has estimated that impacts of comet nuclei, mainly those of long-period orbits, may account for as much as 30% of the Phanerozoic production of impact craters larger than 10 km in diameter. Weissman, on the other hand, estimates that the cratering rate from comet impacts is only about 10% of the total Phanerozoic rate. This difference is due chiefly to differences in the evaluation of sizes of the long-period comet nuclei.

114

b. Asteroids

About 10^3 asteroids brighter than absolute visual magnitude 18 are estimated to move in orbits that permit collision with the Earth. This estimate is based on systematic surveys of the sky for asteroids approaching Earth. Only a few percent of the estimated Earth-crossing population has actually been discovered. At absolute visual magnitude 18, dark asteroids (C-type) have diameters of about 1.7 km, whereas relatively bright (S-type) asteroids have diameters near 0.9 km. One of the principal uncertainties in estimating the cratering rate by asteroid impact is in the determination of the proportion of the C and S photometric types among Earth-crossing bodies. Observational selection effects favor the discovery and measurement of bright objects. The majority of discovered Earth-crossers that have been well observed by photometric and radiometric methods are relatively bright, but most of the large objects, which include the bulk of the mass, appear to be dark C-type objects.

The mean probability of collision with the Earth for individual Earth-crossing asteroids is about 3×10^{-9} yr^{-1}. When multiplied by the estimated population, this yields a collision rate of about three per million years for asteroids brighter than absolute magnitude 18. If half the Earth-crossers of any given magnitude are assumed to be bright S-type asteroids and half are dark C-type bodies, the production of impact craters larger than 10 km in diameter on the continents is estimated at about 2×10^{-14} km^{-2} yr^{-1} (Shoemaker et al., 1979). Within the errors of estimation, this is indistinguishable from the Phanerozoic impact crater record.

The Earth-crossing asteroid swarm is depleted by collisions with the Earth and the other terrestrial planets and by ejection of asteroids from the solar system as a result of successive close encounters with the planets. Typical dynamical lifetimes for these bodies are only about 3×10^7 yr. The swarm would be quickly depleted if the losses were not balanced by the injection of new asteroids into Earth-crossing orbits. The consistency between the present estimated cratering rate and the geologic record of impact back to about 500 myr ago indicates that the population of Earth-crossers is approximately in equilibrium. Analysis of the lunar cratering record suggests that the average flux of impacting bodies during Phanerozoic time may have been about twice as high as the average flux over the past 3.3 byr.

Earth-crossing asteroids are probably derived from two sources. Some are certainly derived from the main asteroid belt and are injected into Earth-crossing orbits by the effects of dynamical resonances and close encounters with Mars. Other Earth-crossers may be extinct very-short-period comets. If a residue or core of rocky material is left when all the ices have sublimated (from a comet such as P/Encke, for example), the object would be recognized at the telescope as an Earth-crossing asteroid. Coarse rocky material may also form a lag deposit on the surface of an ablating comet nucleus which could shut off observable cometary activity and thus give it the appearance of an asteroid.

c. Impact Effects

Comet nuclei and asteroids larger than 1 km in diameter will unequivocally extinguish life locally, wherever they strike the Earth. This direct effect would ordinarily be of significance to biological evolution only if the impact occurred in a refugium crowded with species concentrated there by environmental stresses (e.g., glaciation). As the size of the object increases, however, a threshold is reached at which the material ejected into the high atmosphere may exert a strong transient effect on global climate. Suspension in the stratosphere of a few tenths of a gram of submicron-size dust per square centimeter of Earth's surface would prevent almost all of the sunlight from reaching the ground. Pollack et al. (1983) have estimated that the settling time of most of the stratospheric dust would be on the order of several months to half a year. Under these conditions, only the warming of the air by the heat stored in the oceanic thermosphere would prevent the troposphere from becoming nearly isothermal. In a short time, mean surface temperatures over the continental interiors would drop by several tens of degrees Celsius; coastal areas would experience temperature declines of lesser severity.

A somewhat longer-lived transient climatic effect may be produced by large impacts in the deep ocean. Enough water can be injected into the high atmosphere to replace most of the stratospheric air with water vapor. Emiliani et al. (1981) have suggested that, after the excess water has precipitated and the atmosphere

116

clears, the remaining water vapor would lead to a greenhouse effect that would raise surface temperatures by more than 10°C above the preexisting ambient conditions. This type of transient excursion probably persists for times on the order of years, as the equilibrium composition of the stratosphere would be reestablished only by slow processes of photochemical dissociation of the H_2O and diffusion across the tropopause.

Still other biologically deleterious effects of large impacts may be associated with large quantities of NO_x produced in the high-temperature atmospheric shock wave, and possibly by contamination of the atmosphere by the constituents of the projectile itself. The temperature excursions, a possible deleterious effect on global photosynthesis, and toxic effects of the projectile's constituents have all been considered as potential major exterminators of plant and animal life (Emiliani et al., 1981; Hsü, 1980).

d. Threshold Size

The threshold size of impacting bodies at which biologically significant perturbations of the atmosphere and oceanic thermosphere are produced is very poorly understood. If the abrupt extinction of marine plankton at the end of the Cretaceous Period is related to the impact of a body large enough to produce the observed noble metal anomaly at the Cretaceous-Tertiary boundary (Alvarez et al., 1980), then projectile diameters on the order of 10 km are evidently above the threshold. On the basis of the estimated Phanerozoic cratering rate and the size distribution of post-mare craters on the Moon, 10-km-diam projectiles struck the Earth with a mean frequency of once every 0.5×10^8 yr during Phanerozoic time. From the long-term lunar impact record, the mean frequency of Earth impact of 10-km bodies back to 3.3 byr ago was about once per 10^8 yr.

The threshold size of projectiles that might cause mass extinction of species in certain environments may be considerably smaller than 10 km in diameter. At 5 km in diameter, the frequency of impact is about four times as great as at 10 km. It is entirely possible that dozens of impact-related ecological jolts, each of which was severe enough to be reflected in the paleontologic record, were delivered to the biosphere during the Phanerozoic. A test of this possibility would require close scrutiny of the stratigraphic and paleontologic evidence.

Bodies larger than 10 km in diameter can also hit the Earth. For example, the asteroid 433 Eros approaching Earth has a 20% chance of hitting the Earth in the next 400 myr. The mean diameter of Eros is about 20 km. Over the span of Precambrian time back to 3.3 byr ago, it is likely that several asteroids and comet nuclei with 20- to 30-km diameters struck the Earth. Whether the climatic perturbations produced by these giant impacts were much greater than those produced by 10-km bodies is not yet clear. It may be that climatic perturbations were limited by saturation effects and that any extra material introduced into the atmosphere by giant impacts, exceeding a certain limit, simply fell out again rather quickly. On the other hand, prompt effects, such as the heating of the atmosphere due to compression under the initial load of material, probably have no upper bound.

The lunar crater record shows that the cratering rate was about 25 times higher, 3.9 byr ago, than it is at present, and that it declined approximately exponentially, with a half-life near 10^8 yr, between 3.9 and 3.3 byr ago (fig. III-1). Dozens of objects larger than 20 km in diameter probably struck the Earth in the few hundred million years after deposition of the earliest recorded Precambrian sediments of the Isua Complex in present-day Greenland. At still earlier times, the bombardment was even more intense. If any primitive organisms were in existence at that time, they were probably subjected to frequently repeated environmental insults on a global scale.

2. Secular Changes of the Earth's Orbit, Precession of the Earth's Pole, and Evolution of the Earth-Moon System

a. Orbital and Attitudinal Oscillations of the Earth

Owing to perturbations by the other planets, the orbit of the Earth undergoes continuous changes (Brouwer and Van Woerkom, 1950). The eccentricity of the orbit, at present 0.017, varies between the extreme values of 0 and 0.067. Quasiperiodic oscillations of about 0.02 in eccentricity, with dominant periods on the order of 100,000 yr, are coupled with secular advance in the longitude of perihelion (fig. VI-1). Inclination of the Earth's orbit relative to the invariable plane of the solar system presently varies

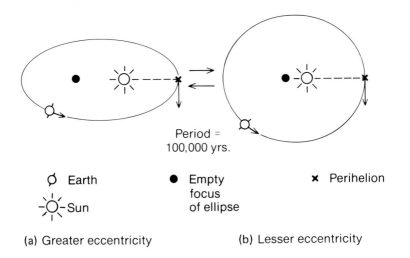

⚴ Earth	● Empty focus of ellipse	✗ Perihelion
☼-Sun		

(a) Greater eccentricity   (b) Lesser eccentricity

Period = 100,000 yrs.

Figure VI-1.— *Quasi-periodic oscillations in the eccentricity of Earth's orbit, and change in the position of the perihelion with respect to a fixed direction in space. Period = 10^5 yr.*

between 0° and 2.92°. Periodic oscillations of about 1° to 2° in inclination are coupled with relatively steady decrease in the longitudes of the nodes of the orbit relative to the invariable plane (fig. VI-2). The secular change of the nodes corresponds to a complex wobbling motion of the ecliptic pole relative to the invariable plane. A complete 360° cycle of regression of the nodes takes about 70,000 yr, on the average.

Gravitational attraction of the Sun and Moon on the equatorial bulge of the Earth causes the rotation axis of the Earth to precess with a nearly uniform period of about 26,000 yr. However, this period beats against an opposed variable precession of the orbital ellipse (perihelion) so that in terms of the latter, the period of the axial precession shows a number of modes, the dominant ones being 19,000 and 23,000 yr. Change in the angle between the pole and the ecliptic is driven by different forces and proceeds at a different frequency from the precession of the Earth's rotational pole (fig. VI-3). The angle between the pole and a line drawn perpendicular to the ecliptic (that is, the obliquity of the ecliptic) changes continuously with a period of 41,000 yr. The present obliquity is 23.45° and is decreasing at the rate of 47.6" per century. The recent mean obliquity is 23.30°; over the last 10^8 yr,

119

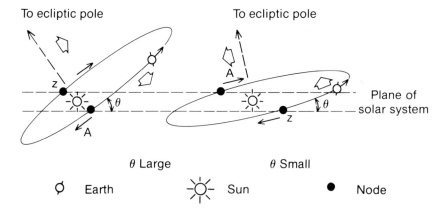

To ecliptic pole   To ecliptic pole

θ Large θ Small

Plane of
solar system

◌ Earth   ☀ Sun   ● Node

Figure VI-2.— *Movement of the nodes of Earth's orbit (intersections with the plane of the solar system) and oscillation of the angle between orbit and plane. Period of node rotation and angle oscillation is about 70,000 yr. The angle shown is much exaggerated.*

its value has varied between extremes of about 20.4° and 26.2°. This 6° fluctuation in obliquity causes significant variation in the amplitude of seasonal climatic differences (fig. VI-4).

Another significant modulation of the climate arises from the change in the orientation of the rotational axis relative to the

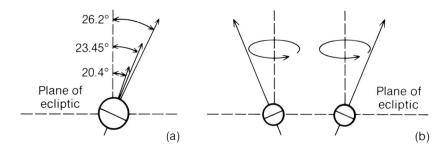

Figure VI-3.— *Periodic changes in the orientation of the rotational axis. (a) Changes in the angle between the Earth's axis and the vertical from the ecliptic plane. Period = 41,000 yr. (b) Precession of the axis (change in the orientation of the Earth without a change in the angle between the Earth's axis and the vertical from the ecliptic plane). Absolute period = 26,000 yr, period relative to elliptical orbit, 19,000–23,000 yr.*

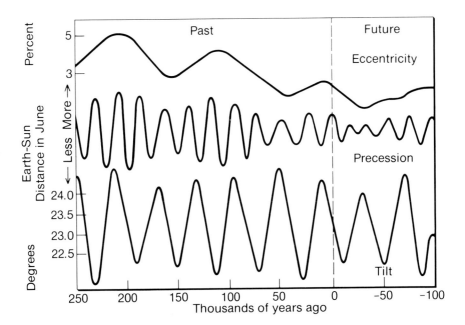

Figure VI-4.— *Combined effects of changes in orbit eccentricity, advance of the position of the perihelion (precession), and changes in the tilt of the Earth with respect to the ecliptic plane. The greater the tilt, the greater the seasonality (summer-winter contrast) in each hemisphere. Eccentricity combined with precession favors first one, then the other, hemisphere in terms of summer insolation in the course of these cycles. (After Imbrie and Imbrie, 1979.)*

longitude of perihelion. When the ecliptic longitude of the north pole is nearly 180° from perihelion, for example (fig. VI-5a), the boreal summer occurs when Earth is nearest the Sun; the seasonal contrast between winter and summer in the northern hemisphere is then enhanced. When the longitudes of the north pole and perihelion are coincident, on the other hand, boreal summers tend to be cooler and winters warmer. These effects are strongest when the orbital eccentricity is highest (fig. VI-1). The variation in difference between the longitudes of perihelion and the rotational pole (sometimes referred to as "precession") is complex, but has dominant frequencies of about 1 cycle/19,000 yr and 1 cycle/23,000 yr. These result from beating of the frequency of true precession of the rotational pole (fig. VI-3b) against the quasiperiodic advance of the longitude of perihelion (fig. VI-1).

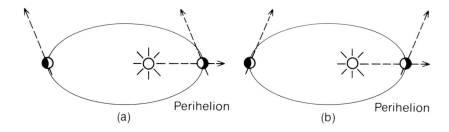

Figure VI-5.— *Orientation of the poles with respect to the perihelion. (a) Boreal summer when Earth is nearest to the Sun. (b) Boreal summer when Earth is farthest from the Sun.*

b. The Milankovitch Mechanism

Milankovitch (1941) showed that these orbital variations cause appreciable change in the insolation of the Earth's hemispheres. He thereby supported early speculations that they might be responsible for the oscillations of the ice caps during the Pleistocene epoch. Global fluctuations in climate are believed to result from the unequal distribution of land masses between the northern and southern hemispheres. As applied to the Pleistocene epoch, the Milankovitch model predicts growth of ice sheets when boreal winters are warm and summers are cool. Net ablation of ice occurs in the opposite situation, when boreal summers are warm and the winters are cool. The effect would be amplified when both the obliquity of the Earth and the eccentricity of its orbit are high.

Examination of the climatic record of the past 500,000 yr, determined primarily by interpretation of deep sea piston cores, confirms that dominant components of frequency of climatic fluctuation do correspond with the principal frequencies that arise from the secular variation of the Earth's orbit and the precession of the Earth's rotational pole (Hays et al., 1976; Imbrie and Imbrie, 1980). The dominant cycle in the climatic record of the late Pleistocene has a period of about 100,000 yr, which corresponds with the 100,000-yr cycle of variation in orbital eccentricity (fig. VI-1). Periods of major glaciation have occurred at times of low eccentricity. A 41,000-yr cycle superimposed on the 100,000-yr cycle of glaciation corresponds to the 41,000-yr period of oscillation in the obliquity of the rotational axis. Glacial maxima correspond to periods of high obliquity, with a phase lag of about 9,000 yr. Finally, subordinate maxima are also correlated with "precession" in the manner predicted by Milankovitch. Some of the spectral power at the observed 100,000-yr climatic period can be simulated by nonlinear models of climatic response to the orbital forcing functions (Imbrie and Imbrie, 1980). Such models are of a formal nature and represent only the first step toward physical understanding. The long-term correlation of glaciation with low eccentricity is poorly understood. Here, continued theoretical work can make major new contributions to our understanding of climatic cycles of the past.

c. Tidal Relationships

Changes in the Earth-Moon relationship have affected the size, inclination, and eccentricity of the Moon's orbit, the length of the lunar month, the period of rotation of the Earth, the period of precession of the Earth's rotation axis, and the mean obliquity of the ecliptic. These dynamic changes arise from phase lags in both the solid-body tides in the Earth and in the oceanic tides. Owing to inelasticity of the Earth and the drag of tidal currents on the sea floor, the tidal maxima are carried forward (in the direction of the Earth's spin) relative to the Earth-Moon axis (fig. VI-6). The

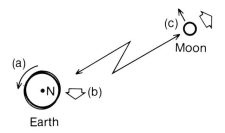

Figure VI-6.— *Earth-Moon relationship responsible for lengthening the Earth's period of rotation, and increasing the Earth-Moon distance. As a result, days are now longer and modern tides are not as high as in the past. (a) Tidal bulge carried forward by the Earth's rotation. (b) Gravitational torque by the Moon on the tidal bulge slows the Earth's rotation. (c) Acceleration of the Moon by the tidal bulge increases its distance from the Earth.*

unequal gravitational attraction of the Moon and the Sun on the tides on opposite sides of the Earth result in a net torque that acts to retard the Earth's rotation. There is also a corresponding acceleration of the Moon; most of the spin angular momentum lost by the Earth is converted to orbital angular momentum of the Moon. The Moon's orbit becomes steadily larger and its period increases as the spin of the Earth slows down.

As the semimajor axis of the Moon's orbit increases, the Moon's orbital inclination relative to the Earth's equatorial plane steadily increases and its inclination relative to the invariable plane of the solar system decreases (Darwin, 1880; Goldreich, 1966). This change is accompanied by a corresponding increase in the inclination of the Earth's equatorial plane to the invariable plane, and hence an increase in the mean obliquity of the ecliptic (fig. VI-7). The principal effects of this "tidal" evolution are that, at earlier periods in Earth history, the day was shorter, oceanic tide ranges were larger, and the mean obliquity was lower. So long as other factors did not predominate, seasonal differences in climate tended to be smaller. As the mean obliquity has increased, the orbital forcing of climatic change has tended to increase.

The extent of tidal evolution of the Earth-Moon system during Phanerozoic time is an unsolved problem. If the present tidal torque is extrapolated backward in time, taking appropriate account of the change of tidal forces with change in Earth-Moon distance, then the Moon would have approached a synchronous orbital altitude between 1 and 2 byr ago (McDonald, 1966). In

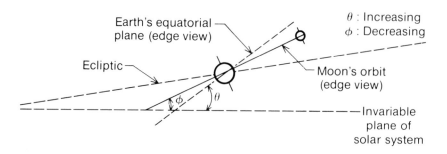

Figure VI-7.— *Changes in obliquity of the Earth resulting from changes in the Earth-Moon orbital relationship. Increase in θ exaggerates the differences between summer and winter weather.*

early Cambrian time, the length of the day would have been about 16 hr, tide ranges would have been about 30% larger than their present values, and the mean obliquity would have been about 2° lower. (For various recent calculations of changes in the Earth-Moon system, see McDonald, 1964, 1966; Goldreich, 1966.) It is highly unlikely that the Earth-Moon system has followed the historical course predicted by this simple extrapolation, however. At present, a significant fraction of the torque arises from dissipation of oceanic tides, and the secular acceleration of the Moon is strongly dependent on tidal dissipation in shallow water on the continental shelves (Munk and McDonald, 1960). The rate of change of the Moon's orbit, of the Earth's spin rate, and of the tilt of the Earth's axis is dependent, in other words, on the configuration of continental land masses and on sea level, both of which have been highly variable over geologic time. The actual history of the Earth-Moon system will have to be solved from independent observations of the sedimentary or paleontologic record that reveal the number of days in the year, days in the month, or months in the year at various points in geologic time.

3. Effects of Changes in the Sun

a. Climatic Sensitivity to Solar Output

There can be no question that life on Earth utterly depends upon sunlight and, within rather narrow limits, on the constancy of the Sun. Sunlight provides almost all of the essential ingredients for life, including heat, light, energy, and the replenishment of oxygen through photosynthesis. The Sun is the principal driving force for the circulation of the air and the oceans, and for the hydrologic cycle that dominates physical and chemical processes on the surface of the planet. It is the ultimate energy source for all the varied phenomena known as "weather." The equilibrium temperatures of the air, the seas, and the land are directly proportional to the amount of solar energy received. Modern climate models establish that a change of 1% in the total flux of solar radiation (the "solar constant") would alter the surface temperature by 1° to 2°C. The same models strongly suggest that a decrease of no more than 5% in solar flux would provoke a major ice age, and that a drop of 10% would be catastrophic, in the sense that the entire Earth would then be permanently covered with ice. Because of the high albedo of ice, the frozen Earth would thaw only after a subsequent increase of 30% in the brightness of the Sun (Schneider and Dickinson, 1974; Newkirk, 1980).

b. Likelihood of Solar Change

All that we know of the Sun suggests that major changes in its energetic outputs are unlikely. Today, in any given year, the solar constant varies through a range of no more than a few tenths of 1% (as established by modern space-borne measurements). It may have varied between limits of perhaps ±1% during the last millenium (but probably no more than that), and indeed there is little if any evidence to suggest that the Sun has ever experienced drastic or catastrophic changes. Present theory strongly suggests that the Sun's luminosity gradually increased by about 30% over its 4.6 byr lifetime (Newkirk, 1980). Thus the Precambrian Sun should have been only 70–80% as bright as it is today. This, as suggested by climate models, would have been inadequate to keep water in a liquid state anywhere on the surface of the Earth. This conclusion is, of course, at odds with the main body of geologic evidence; there is no indication that the earliest life forms were born in ice or that the Earth was ever wholly ice-covered. One escape from this paradox of a "faint early Sun" is possible if one postulates a Precambrian atmosphere containing gases that gave the Earth a more heat-retentive "greenhouse" environment than exists at present. In any case, early life on Earth almost certainly evolved under the light of a Sun that was slightly smaller, appreciably dimmer, and significantly redder than is the one that we see in the sky today. Solar infrared radiation would have been enhanced, and shortwave emissions would have been reduced, relative to the visible portion of the spectrum. With an effective temperature of about 5300 K (as opposed to 5800 K today), the peak emission would have been shifted about 470 Å toward longer wavelengths, making the Sun appear deep red as opposed to yellow-white today. What effects these subtle changes might have had on biological processes depend critically upon the radiative properties of the atmosphere at the time. These are poorly known, if known at all. Interestingly, chlorophyll, which evolved early in Earth's history, utilizes the red portion of the Sun's spectrum for photosynthesis.

A newly proposed theoretical possibility of very-long-term changes in the radiative output of the Sun stems from attempts to explain the apparent deficit in solar neutrino flux. As suggested by Dilke and Gough (1972), instabilities in the deep interior of the Sun may provoke recurrent periods of episodic mixing that stir together the two principal ingredients of the solar core, hydrogen and helium. At these times the rate of solar energy generation (and hence the eventual luminosity of the Sun) would be perturbed. The solar constant would first drop by about 5–7%. Then it would slowly recover and "overshoot." The recurrence period of such episodes is calculated to be about 300 myr, with the last episode occurring some 3 myr ago. If real, these suspected changes in solar luminosity would have inescapable terrestrial effects. A drop in luminosity 3 myr ago clearly would have favored the onset of the present ice age. Such proposed solar changes have been related to a purported period of about 250 myr in ice age recurrence.

Traditionally, changes in the amount of land area, in its relief, and in its position relative to the poles, have been considered responsible for ice ages because of changes in the albedo feedback mechanism (Donn and Shaw, 1977). At this time, there seems to be no good reason to abandon this view. By itself, the indirect impact of solar mixing episodes on the development of life would probably be minor.

Little is known about periodic secular solar variability recurring at intervals intermediate between that of episodic solar mixing (about 300 myr) and that of the well-established solar magnetic cycle (22 yr). Significant solar variations with periods ranging from 100 yr to 100 myr may indeed exist. Our limited knowledge of the past history of the Sun, however, is only just sufficient to begin a serious search for various yet-unrecognized variations that probably do occur on long time scales (Frazier, 1981). The gap in our knowledge of solar cycles is illustrated in figure VI-8.

c. Historical Records

Accounts from the last millenium of recorded history leave little doubt that displays of the aurora and the occurrence of sunspots (seen with the naked eye) vary secularly in irregular episodes of roughly 100 to 1000 yr duration (Eddy, 1980; fig. VI-9). This apparent secular variability in solar activity is clearly confirmed by precision analyses of tree-ring radiocarbon that now extend about

127

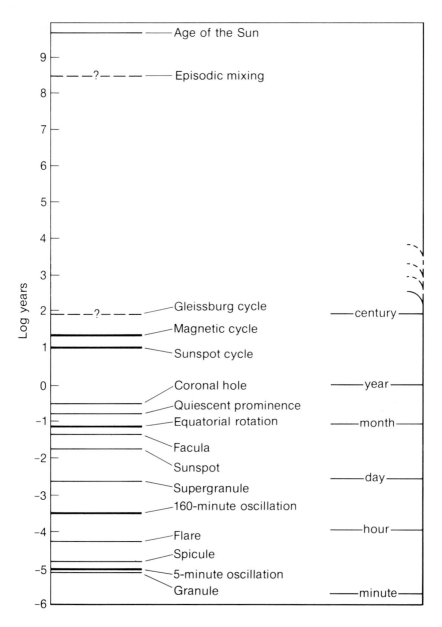

Figure VI-8.— *Time scales of known solar events. "Gleissburg cycle" is a purported period of 60–90 yr, recognized in the envelope of the curve of annual mean sunspot number, and in auroral records. A gap exists in our knowledge of events on scales of 10^2–10^8 yr. (After Geophysics Study Committee; reproduced from "Solar Variability, Weather and Climate, National Academy Press, Washington, D.C., 1982.)*

128

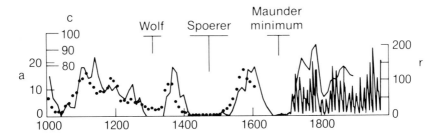

Figure VI-9.— *Various measures of solar activity during the last 1000 yr. Dark circles, auroral reports per decade, scale "a" at left. Solid line, relative decrease in C^{14} production rate, scale "c" at left. (After Stuiver and Quay, Science, vol. 207, 1980, pp. 11–19, copyright 1980 by the American Association for the Advancement of Science.) Fine jagged line, annual mean sunspot number, scale "r" at right. (After Geophysics Study Committee; reproduced from Solar Variability, Weather and Climate, National Academy Press, Washington, D.C., 1982.)*

7500 yr into the past. The analysis of dated ice and sea cores and the use of other radio-isotopes with longer half-lives (such as beryllium-10) promise a longer look at the last several million years of solar behavior. With isotopic sampling, however, we probe rather subtle effects of solar behavior; not necessarily the flux of heat and light, but conditions in the solar wind, the continuous flow of atomic particles from the outer corona of the Sun. Solar wind particles carry a negligible fraction of the total energy output of the Sun. Moreover, they lose their energy in the uppermost atmosphere of the Earth. Changes in sunspots or solar wind conditions may eventually provide a clue to subtle changes in the total energy output of the Sun, but such connections have yet to be clearly demonstrated. In any case, aurorae, sunspots, and the solar wind have little direct effect on organisms that live on the surface of the Earth, and a minor effect on the weather, at most. Recurrent periods of depressed solar activity like the Maunder Minimum (AD 1645–1715; fig. VI-9) correspond roughly with eras of possible climatic cooling, of perhaps 1°C in global average. Sophisticated analyses suggest a possible surface temperature modulation of about one-tenth of this amount due to the 11-yr sunspot cycle and a possible circulation-induced drought cycle of 22 yr that may also be related to the magnetic cycle of the Sun (Geophysics Study Committee, 1982).

4. Supernovae, Cosmic Radiation, and Galactic Rotation

a. Supernovae

Certain stars end their lives in cataclysmic supernova eruptions. If a supernova were to occur near the Earth, it could have measurable (if not deadly) effects on life on the planet.

The evolutionary development of a star is thought to be a simple function of its mass. Stars that are about one and one-half times as massive as the Sun, or larger, are the most likely supernova candidates. About one star in a hundred falls in this category. We see spectacular supernova eruptions infrequently, mainly because of the vast distances of most stars from us, the relative scarcity of appropriate stars, and the long lifetimes of stars.

A supernova erupts with a dramatic flash of visible light and an even greater enhancement of radiation in the far ultraviolet and X-ray region. The eruptive phases of distant supernovae were witnessed by early European astronomers in AD 1604 (in the constellation Ophiuchus) and 1572 (in Cassiopeia), and by Chinese astronomers in AD 1054 (in the constellation Taurus) (Clark, 1979). A more dramatic example that also would have been visible from the Earth is the great supernova that is thought to have erupted in the southern constellation Vela about 11,000 yr ago, at a distance of about 1500 light years (Asimov, 1979; Brandt et al., 1971). A remnant veil of stellar debris that is still expanding outward from the site of that explosion can be detected by modern astronomical instruments. For several days the Vela supernova would have been as bright as the full Moon. It would have been visible in daylight for several weeks. At a distance of 1500 lt-yr, the principal effect of the Vela explosion on the Earth was probably that of creating a prehistoric spectacle in the sky. Had this exploding star been as near as 10 lt-yr, however, the visible and infrared radiation would have impinged upon the surface of the Earth as a stellar heat wave of many weeks' duration (Asimov, 1979). This flood of heat and light would have added 10–20% to the radiation of the Sun, with possible major climatic effects, including, perhaps, the melting of polar ice. The upper atmosphere of the Earth would have been exposed to a blast of X-rays lasting several weeks, which in turn would certainly have altered the chemistry and transmission characteristics of the atmosphere for some time. As would be true of the X-ray surge, most of the supernova's ultraviolet flux would also have been absorbed high in the atmosphere. Enough of the near-ultraviolet (3000–4000 Å wavelength) would reach the surface of the Earth, however, to be felt as "starburn," with possible malignant effects on unsheltered species.

The most damaging effect of a nearby supernova would not be caused by the wave of light and heat, but rather by the delayed and protracted arrival of a cloud of high-energy cosmic rays (Tucker, 1981). For one hundred to perhaps several thousand years, depending upon the nature of the supernova eruption, the Earth would be bathed in a potentially lethal wave of intense particle radiation, much like that following a nuclear explosion. Terry and Tucker (1968) considered the probable effects upon life of a supernova at a distance of 16 lt-yr and concluded that the high-energy particle radiation from such an event, reaching levels possibly 12 orders of magnitude greater than the steady-state cosmic ray flux received from the Sun today, would be adequate to kill higher life forms. Dosages would be greatest at high altitudes and at high latitudes. The Earth's atmosphere and oceans would provide some protection, but the effect of damaging radiation on living things and on the development of life would certainly be significant.

A supernova might be expected to explode within 100 lt-yr of the Earth about every 750 myr, or about five times during the history of the planet (Tucker, 1981). A very close eruption, say within 10 lt-yr, is much less probable, but it is still possible. Even distant supernovae could produce damaging effects on life. Terry and Tucker (1968) have estimated that life-damaging dosages of radiation can be expected from supernova explosions as often as every 10 myr.

The biological effects of dramatic short-period enhancements in cosmic radiation would be significantly increased if the supernova eruption occurred at the time of a reversal in the Earth's magnetic field. At such times, when the field strength drops by an order of magnitude (Reid, 1976), charged particles could reach the Earth's surface at low latitudes with greater ease. The damaging effects on life in the tropical and temperate zones would then be at a maximum. The terrestrial magnetic field reverses itself at irregular intervals. The longest time between past occurrences is tens of millions of years, and the shortest is about 50,000 yr. Reversals are approximately as unpredictable as supernova eruptions. The most drastic impact of a blast of cosmic rays from a supernova would result, therefore, from a chance coincidence of two unlikely events: a nearby supernova explosion at the time of a terrestrial field reversal. Such a coincidence, although highly improbable, is still possible, and could exceed the destructive capacity of any other extraterrestrial event, including the impact of a very large asteroid.

b. Galactic Clouds

Another extraterrestrial phenomenon that could perturb life on Earth is the passage of the Sun and solar system through a dense cloud in the galaxy. The spiral arms of the galaxy are non-uniform concentrations of gas and dust, which exist as density waves through which stars like the Sun must pass in their revolutions about the galactic center. The Sun, at a distance of about 30,000 lt-yr from the center, orbits the galaxy in about 250 myr. Periods of about this length have been noted in paleo-climate reconstructions, leading to suggestions that the passage of the Sun through regions of particularly dense matter may alter the effective temperature of the star, either by the accretion of interstellar matter or by the simple diminution of sunlight (McCrea, 1975, 1976). The sketchy record of changes in terrestrial climate, occurring on these time scales, suggests that encounters with galactic dust and gas concentrations may be influential in causing the onsets of periods of major glaciation. This hypothesis is only a preliminary one. Our understanding is currently impeded by the fact that the galaxy probably has many dense spiral arms that may be encountered by the solar system. Their numbers and positions are not known, nor are the periodicities with which the Sun and planets might encounter them.

C. THE EVOLUTIONARY SIGNIFICANCE OF EXTRATERRESTRIAL PHENOMENA

The phenomena described in the preceding sections are all capable of influencing the course of biological evolution. Their effects can be unique, periodic, or persistent, and can intrude upon the environments of living organisms in many ways. Subtle alteration of DNA by enhancement of the radiation background, indirect reorientation of natural selection by alterations of global climate, and direct overt extinction of plants and animals as a consequence of particularly cataclysmic events are among the many evolutionary side effects of disturbances that originate in space. In the text that follows, we have evaluated these phenomena, both in terms of their probable relative importance as agents for perturbation of evolution, and in terms of their amenability to research.

This assessment was a tricky and preliminary undertaking. In so doing, we considered the probable frequency of occurrence of each phenomenon, its potential impact on the history of life, and evidence that each phenomenon has actually exerted an effect during the Earth's past. We also considered whether techniques are available for the study of each phenomenon. One might object to this pragmatic approach on philosophical grounds. However, without appropriate techniques we are unlikely to detect evidence of the effectiveness of a particular phenomenon, even if it happens to be an important one. We are confident that the passage of time will result in the development of new investigative techniques that are capable of dealing with problems that now appear to be intractable. In some cases (for example, our discussion of Be^{10} records as potentially indicative of past solar variability), we considered certain areas in which these advances might occur. Recognizing that such developments may eventually reorder our list, we have assigned priorities to the extraterrestrial phenomena as shown in table VI-1.

The study of *asteroid impacts* was assigned the highest priority. The probability of the impact of large planetesimals upon the Earth can be estimated with reasonable accuracy, both from studies of the geologic record and from the observed abundance of eligible objects combined with celestial mechanical calculations. About 10 large objects (10 km or more in diameter) probably hit the Earth during Phanerozoic time; this is sufficient to warrant consideration of the possibility of at least one serious modification of the course of evolution in the sense now commonly postulated for the Cretaceous-Tertiary boundary (Alvarez et al., 1980; Emiliani et al., 1981). This particular boundary event suggests a score of "high" for the potential for the disturbance of evolution by an impact and a score of "strong" for convincing evidence that

133

TABLE VI-1.— TYPES OF EXTRATERRESTRIAL PHENOMENA CONSIDERED, AND THEIR RELATIVE IMPORTANCE

Phenomenon	Probable number of Phanerozoic occurrences	Potential effect on evolution	Evidence for past influence on Earth environments	Suitability of existing research techniques	Weighted priority for NASA research
Asteroid and comet impact	10 impacts	High	Strong	Good	100
Orbital effects	3 ice ages	Medium	Strong	Good	33
Solar variation	2 dim phases	High	Weak	Fair	10
Supernovae	1 explosion	High	Weak	Fair	3
Galactic density waves	3 encounters	Low	Weak	Poor	1

asteroid impacts actually do exert such disturbances. Asteroid impacts may also provide synchronous global benchmarks in geologic strata. The great significance of such benchmarks to the interpretation of the history of life has been mentioned in chapter III. The geological, paleontological, and chemical techniques for detecting and studying impact phenomena are also well developed (Hsü et al., 1982; Thierstein, 1980). For all of these reasons, the study of asteroid impacts was assigned a very high priority.

Orbital effects, with their potential for altering global climates, were ranked second. The "probable number of occurrences" due to orbital effects shown in table VI-1 refers to the number of ice ages in the Phanerozoic. Such episodes influence evolution in many significant ways. We have already mentioned (chapters IV and V) the profound indirect effects of changing sea levels, which accompany continental glaciations, upon marine and terrestrial faunas. Direct effects may also occur, perhaps contributing to extinctions, perhaps contributing to speciation via the fragmentation of species ranges. We certainly know that the last ice age affected the physical environment in a most dramatic manner. It was accompanied by a dramatic extinction of large mammals, and witnessed the final explosive phase of the cultural, technological, and biological development of human beings. The techniques for the study of such effects are well developed (Flint, 1971; Hays et al., 1976; Emiliani, 1978). The potential for the impact of orbital variations upon evolution, the evidence that such effects have been important in the past, and the availability of refined techniques prompt us to assign high priority to the study of those effects.

The other extraterrestrial factors *(solar variability, supernova radiation,* and *galactic density waves)* were ranked substantially lower than were the two leading ones. They are not necessarily unimportant, but their potential for influencing the development of life on the Earth is poorly understood, and evidence of their operation in the past is difficult to detect in the geologic record. The theory of the physics of solar energy generation is now somewhat in question as a result of anomalous neutrino fluxes that have been measured (Davis and Evans, 1978). The outcome of this revision may suggest new directions for research in this important area — a development that could raise the priority of solar studies in this context. Star densities, stellar evolutionary rates, and other considerations suggest that supernovae have probably been too far away from the Earth to play a major role in the development of Phanerozoic life (Tucker, 1981). The effects of galactic density waves, finally, are poorly known and would be virtually indistinguishable, in the geologic record, from those of solar variability at present. These low-ranked phenomena may have exerted significant unique or periodic effects upon the evolution of complex life that are presently unrecognized. Their potential as factors in the evolutionary story, both on Earth and on other planets, should not be underestimated.

D. RESEARCH RECOMMENDATIONS

Recommendation 1. Impact Effects

One means of advancing our understanding of the evolution of complex life is to correlate changes in the physical environment with evolutionary changes in organisms. This may prove to be most feasible for intervals that saw rapid evolutionary change, coincident with sudden environmental change of the sort that accompanies a large asteroid impact. The Cretaceous-Tertiary boundary provides the first strong evidence of this type of coincidence. An obvious strategy is to apply the asteroid model of extinction to other parts of the Phanerozoic record, and to cast research proposals in the image of the scenario developed by Luis Alvarez and co-workers. Of course, we must also study counter-examples; namely, evidence of asteroid impacts that were unaccompanied by evolutionary events, and episodes of extinction that are not associated with asteroid impacts.

The Cretaceous termination scenario (Alvarez et al., 1980; Emiliani et al., 1981; Pollack et al., 1983), although not accepted *in toto* by the paleontologic community, suggests some specific approaches to the assessment of impact effects. Environmental conditions before and after major impact events should be documented. This includes physical-chemical evidence pertaining to the nature of the climate before and after the impact, and biological information bearing upon the same subject. We should identify those organisms that died at about the time of each impact event and those that survived, and determine whether the extinctions were actually coincident with the event. In particular, we might deduce the environmental preferences of the surviving organisms from studies of their nearest living relatives, from their functional anatomies, from the structures of their communities, and from other evidence. Evolutionary change before and after the event should be documented, including rates of origin and background extinction of vertebrate taxa.

Major geological boundaries, particularly those that offer the most nearly complete fossil records, should be examined for evidence of asteroid impacts. This applies to all Period and Epoch boundaries. Boundary strata should be extensively tested for iridium accumulations and, preferably, for other trace elements known to be associated with impacts. Osmium, gold, platinum, and nickel have been suggested (Turekian, 1982), and other elements may prove to be useful. It is equally important that traces of iridium be sought in nonboundary strata. Minor boundaries should also be studied to test hypotheses about extinctions in the absence of impacts, as should evidence of impacts with an absence of associated extinctions. The possibility of synergistic control on extinction should be considered. Adverse preconditioning of the environment by climatic and other factors (resulting, for example, in declines in sea level) might cause an amplification of adverse impact effects. Such considerations will lead into the probability calculus of coincidences.

On the planetary level of investigation, we should document the history of cratering on the Earth and on its neighbors in space. As noted above, results available so far show that the rate of cratering has been uneven through time.

The long-term shift in the size distribution of impacting objects and in the frequency of impact are of interest in this context. How large is the pool of bodies available in the outer solar system, and at what rate has it been depleted? Have there been changes in the rates of disturbance, or the nature of the disturbing sources, that activated these bodies for potential impact on the inner planets? In principle, it should be possible to devise a model of the history of asteroid impacts, based upon the characteristics of the pool and the probability of its disturbance.

Modeling the impacts of large asteroids on the Earth's surface is akin to modeling the effects of large nuclear explosions. In the terminal Cretaceous example, for instance, it was found that the impact of a 10-km body would raise enough dust to obscure sunlight for 1–6 months (Pollack et al., 1983). The energy liberated by this impact is about one million times larger than that of the largest nuclear explosion for which data are available, and about a thousand times larger than that of the largest volcanic event observed in sufficient detail. Thus there is a problem of scale. However, there may be ways other than detonation of nuclear devices to test the hypothesis that dust remains in the stratosphere long after a large explosion. The ice of Greenland and Antarctica probably preserves a record of the fallout of volcanic dust following major volcanic events. Information in the literature on deep-sea sediments reveals the scale of lateral transport of volcanic ash, which is relevant to this question. An ash layer in the North Atlantic, for example, deposited about 9000 yr ago, may be present in the North Pacific. A systematic search for contemporaneous ash layers, and their analysis, would allow an assessment of dust transport distances.

The hypothesis that a cometary impact introduced poison (HCN) in the Earth's environment has been advanced by Hsü (1980). Although this possibility has been considered remote (Thierstein, 1980), it is certainly true that we know little about the possible significance of chemical changes induced by cometary impacts. The chemistry of comets is poorly known, a problem that presently makes it difficult to delineate the details of their effects upon the chemistry of the oceans and the atmosphere.

In summary, much remains to be learned of the nature and frequency of impact events, and of their effects upon life. Research that would remedy this deficiency includes an examination of the fossil and geochemical records at major and minor geological boundaries, a study of cratering histories of the Earth and its planetary neighbors, studies of records of volcanic dust dispersal preserved in polar and glacial ice and deep sea sediments, and modeling of interactions between impacting bodies, the hydrosphere, and living communities.

Recommendation 2: Orbital Parameters

a. The Milankovitch Mechanism

In essence, Milankovitch's hypothesis says that the seasonal distribution of radiation in northern latitudes is crucial to the extent of snow cover in sensitive areas. Through albedo-feedback (the reflection of sunlight by snow), minor differences in the distribution of radiation can be translated into considerable episodes of cooling and warming, extended over long periods of time. In recent years, strong circumstantial evidence has accumulated to support the idea that the climatic fluctuations of the late Pleistocene were indeed driven by precession of the Earth's rotational axis combined with variations in the Earth's orbit. It is well established, for example, that the last deglaciation (and others before it) occurred during a period of maximal summer warming. Conversely, glaciations occur during periods of cooling summers.

The periodicities contained in the Pleistocene record are those of precession (19,000 and 26,000 yr), obliquity (41,000 yr), and eccentricity variation (about 100,000 yr). Precession acts only in conjunction with eccentricity: with a circular orbit, precession has no effect on the passage of the seasons. The exact distribution of energy between these periods (the "power spectrum") is a matter of active research. One may speculate, with respect to evolution, that different periods may act as filters for different taxa, depending upon the evolutionary rates of the taxa considered.

138

While precession and orbital changes have exerted a persistent effect throughout most of geologic history, their effect becomes extremely important when it is augmented by amplifying subsystems. To be precise, correlations between calculated Milankovitch frequencies and observed climatic variations deteriorate for times that are 500,000 yr or more in the past. Those times were ones in which climatic excursions were characterized by lower amplitudes. Before 3 myr ago, when no ice caps existed in the northern hemisphere, amplitudes of climatic excursions were even lower, and the effects of the Milankovitch Mechanism are difficult to detect. One might argue, therefore, that the Milankovitch-driven climatic fluctuations of the late Pleistocene epoch were partially dependent upon positive feedback from sources other than orbital and precessional changes. These might include the initial formations of ice masses, the accumulation of freshwater surface layers on isolated seas, buildups of organic carbon masses, and other developments on the Earth's surface resulting from continental drift and other strictly endogenous factors. If these developments happen to occur at appropriate moments in the Milankovitch cycle, then positive feedback may occur, with the Milankovitch Mechanism reinforcing the factors that were responsible for the initial buildup (or melting) of icecaps in the first place.

From a geologic point of view, it is necessary to identify intervals of rapid climatic change, forced by the Milankovitch Mechanism, that were characterized by extinctions during the Pleistocene. The deglaciation intervals are prime candidates for this search. The effect of the climatic changes upon extinction and evolution has to be assessed and, if positive feedback proves to be essential, it would be desirable to determine the sources of positive feedback that are capable of augmenting the rapid changes promoted by the Milankovitch Mechanism.

At present, orbital changes of the past can be calculated with great accuracy. For times prior to about 0.5 myr ago, geologic dating becomes too uncertain to allow confident comparison of inferred climatic conditions with expected Milankovitch effects. Increased accuracy in dating can facilitate such comparisons; on the other hand, increased understanding of the Milankovitch effects may allow improved geologic dating.

The most promising geologic periods for testing the calculated Milankovitch parameters are those that contain evidence for strong positive feedback, or climatic instability, or both. The Miocene-Pliocene boundary interval is one such time period. The Eocene-Oligocene transition may be another. In the Mesozoic era, no such times may exist. Milankovitch cycles, however, seem to be recognizable (Schwarzacher and Fischer, 1982). In the Paleozoic Era, we must examine the glacial intervals to identify the possible occurrence of cycles (fig. IV-3).

b. Earth-Moon System

The tides generated by the Moon and the Sun form part of the environmental background within which evolution has occurred. As stated earlier, the influence of background events, although crucial in some instances, is difficult to assess. For example, we cannot presently estimate the extent to which the broad features of the evolution of marine life have been determined by events in the intertidal zone, partly because we know of no time in Earth history during which the intertidal zone was absent.

The effects of tides have varied through time. The tides interact with the continental shelves, such that low shelf angles promote large intertidal zones and vice versa. Widespread flooding of the shelves is a consequence of low-lying continents. Intertidal zones will be large during such intervals. Marine biotic diversity was indeed high during times of continental flooding, but did the greater extent of the intertidal zones make the difference? To some extent comparisons of the marine communities of tideless seas (such as the Mediterranean) with those of comparable antiquity in comparable seas with large tide ranges can help to clarify the significance of tides as factors in evolution. Deductions from such comparisons may always be rather tentative, however.

From a geologic point of view, it would be useful to know whether subtidal organisms tend to invade the intertidal zone more often than intertidal organisms move into subtidal water. This can be determined by examining modern communities with a view to deducing ancestor/descendant relationships, and by determining the respective environmental preferences of those organisms.

The rhythms introduced by the Moon's orbit play a large role in governing the behavior of marine organisms (including pelagic ones) as well as terrestrial organisms (including man). It may be possible to determine, from the paleontologic record, just when this "zeitgeber" ("time-giver") appeared in the history of life.

Certain fossil corals appear to preserve growth rings that reveal the number of days in the Paleozoic year (Wells, 1963; Runcorn, 1975). The counting and interpretation of these rings has been difficult. Modern technology can solve this problem objectively and efficiently by digitizing the images of growth layers and analyzing them by power spectrum techniques. Changes in the length of the lunar month, and changes in the number of days per year, should thus be recoverable. Recent studies raise the possibility that lengths of lunar months, numbers of days per year, and even the angle of tilt of the Earth can be determined from stromatolite growth layers for dates in Precambrian time (Vanyo and Awramik, 1982).

There is a direct relationship between lunar cycles, as recorded in fossil shells and sediments, and the distribution of angular momentum in the Earth-Moon system. In turn, the obliquity of Earth's axis is tied to this distribution. Thus, certain fossils can yield data that are essential for assessing the operation of the Milankovitch Mechanism for times ranging, perhaps, to 850 myr in the past.

Recommendation 3: Solar Radiation

It would be highly desirable if we could reconstruct the history of the radiative output of the Sun as a function of wavelength. However, it is difficult to imagine ways of recovering the information needed to do so. A comparative climatological study of Earth and Mars might reveal a record of fluctuating solar output (if it occurred) affecting both planets simultaneously and distinct from effects arising from the orbital and other individual peculiarities of either planet. However, it would be difficult to date and to correlate climatic records for Mars until we have devised better ways of doing so for the Earth.

The history of formation of a radioactive isotope of carbon (C^{14}), which can be determined from tree rings and from deposits that can be dated independently, has been used as another approach to estimating changes in the Sun's radiative output. Radiocarbon is produced in the atmosphere by the bombardment

141

of N^{14} with cosmic rays. The abundance of the latter is influenced by the solar luminosity. The chief problem is that the radiocarbon method is valid only for the last 50,000 yr or so. Before that time, the C^{14} signal is masked by "noise," and there is no good dated material whose C^{14} content can be unequivocally related to atmospheric content. Much of the noise is produced by changes in carbon reservoir sites; these changes are themselves difficult to assess. In another development, the advent of mass spectroscopy for radiocarbon might make it possible to measure the activity of CO_2 trapped in polar ice over the last 100,000 yr. This may provide a much improved basis for assessing the variability of the Sun.

The radioisotope Be^{10}, with a much longer half-life than that of C^{14}, holds some promise in this context. Its production is also modulated by cosmic magnetic field intensity and solar activity. Its geochemical pathways are even less well understood than are those of carbon, however. Thus, changes in the concentration of Be^{10} in deep-sea sediments, for example, cannot as yet be related in an unambiguous manner to changes in magnetic field intensity or solar luminosity.

Fluctuations in the O^{18} values of polar ice have been interpreted as indicators of variations in solar output (Neftel et al., 1982). If a history of solar variability could be established from the ice record, we could then compare it with one that may be recoverable from glacio-lacustrine sediments and from salt deposits of the Permian period and even of the Precambrian era. Any change in the solar output and spectrum through geologic time, as deduced by these methods, should provide valuable new boundary conditions for solar physicists to improve solar models. In turn, a better understanding of changes in the intensity of solar radiation throughout portions of the history of complex life would enhance our understanding of paleoclimates and other attributes of the Phanerozoic Earth.

Recommendation 4: Supernovae and Galactic Effects

It has been suggested that supernova events could explain extinctions (Russell and Tucker, 1971; Schindewolf, 1954). However, their low probability of occurrence in the immediate vicinity of the solar system makes the study of supernova events difficult.

An additional difficulty is that evidence of the past occurrences of supernovae would be difficult to detect in the geologic record. Perhaps unusual abundances of Be^{10} in ice cores (or other isotopes generated by cosmic radiation) could be used for this purpose. Astronomical observations of the present-day sky, including other galaxies, would certainly refine our estimates of the expected frequency of these explosions at distances likely to influence evolution. Another valuable approach would involve modeling the effect of supernova radiation on the atmosphere, terrestrial climates, and living things. If supernova radiation could be shown to impose a pattern of extinction that differs from that created by asteroid impacts, climatic changes, and other events, then supernovae of the past could be detected via their "extinction signatures." The danger of circularity in this approach, however, must be recognized.

An argument has been made that glaciations are cyclic phenomena with a period of about 250 myr, and that the rotation of our galaxy may be partially responsible (Steiner and Grillmair, 1973). One scenario envisions the solar system traveling through dust clouds that periodically attenuate the Sun's radiation. Even though this hypothesis is not compelling at present, it would be desirable to back-track the Sun's path with respect to other galactic regions to determine whether or not the solar system traversed unusual galactic neighborhoods in the past and, if so, to determine the dates of such encounters. Reconstructing the history of the Sun's travels would also provide clues to the likelihood of past perturbations of the cloud of comets surrounding the solar system, as might occur during close passage of other stars. As mentioned previously, disturbances of this cloud can give rise to episodes of impact events on the Earth and on the other planets.

CHAPTER VII
COMPLEX LIFE ELSEWHERE IN SPACE

D. H. Milne, J. Billingham, and D. A. Russell

A. PRELIMINARY DEDUCTIONS ABOUT EXTRATERRESTRIAL LIFE

The subject of extraterrestrial life has fascinated people from all walks of life for many centuries. But only in recent years have we understood enough of astronomy, the planetary sciences, chemistry, and biology to develop closely focused ideas about the possible nature and distribution of life elsewhere in the universe. These ideas provide the basis for an ongoing dialogue in the scientific community.

Many arguments can be made to support the view that life is abundant in the universe. These have been well developed and recorded in many articles, books, and reviews (see, for example, Shklovskii and Sagan, 1966; Billingham, 1981; and references therein), and are essentially as follows. Modern astrophysical and astronomical theory predicts that stars accompanied by orbiting bodies, including planets, are the rule rather than the exception, and that they may well number in the tens of billions in our galaxy alone. Given a suitable location and environment for any single planet, theories of chemical evolution and the origin of life suggest that life is likely to arise spontaneously. Once life has become established on the planetary surface (and given a subsequent period of comparative environmental stability), life may then become complex, more or less rapidly, as a result of evolutionary processes. In some instances, these processes can lead to intelligence, cultural evolution, and science and technology, as they did on the Earth.

An obvious way to study extraterrestrial life is to go to the planets upon which it might be found and to examine it there. Explorations in the 1970s have begun this process within our solar system, and the next century may find us able to send probes to planetary systems of nearby stars. But studies of the past few decades have also revealed that something can be learned about extraterrestrial life from research conducted here on the Earth. The earliest findings have resulted largely from astrophysical research. For example, life is unlikely to have evolved in the very early history of the universe, on planets that formed before carbon, oxygen, nitrogen, and other biogenic elements became widely available. If the oldest stars in the universe are accompanied by planets, therefore, these are likely to be hydrogen-rich gas giants. It seems unlikely that any of those planets would be occupied by indigenous living things. It is also reasonably certain that living things will not be found on planets orbiting O-type stars (Shklovskii and Sagan, 1966; Janes, 1981). Astrophysical observations and theory indicate that such stars probably originate, burn at a steady rate, then "burn out" in a violent manner in much less time than is needed for the spontaneous origin of even the simplest living things. There is not enough time for life to develop in their vicinities. On the other hand, it is not unlikely that the planets of stars of types F, G, and K (which are more similar to the Sun and which constitute about 15% of the stars in the galaxy) might provide substrates for the development of complex life (Shklovskii and Sagan, 1966). The long main-sequence lifetimes of such stars, the fairly broad zones in their vicinities in which planets can exist with surfaces suitable for the presence of liquid water, and other factors suggest that planets with the long periods of comparative environmental stability needed for the evolution of complex life might be found in orbit about them. In these and in other ways, astronomical research has helped to delineate those parts of the cosmos in which a search for life might be conducted.

B. POSSIBLE CONTRIBUTIONS OF EVOLUTIONARY THEORY

1. Probable Evolutionary Outcomes

To astronomical findings such as these, we may now begin to add new insights from a more critical study of biological evolution, of climatology, and of chemical and physical environments on the Earth's surface. In other words, we may be able to extend the questions asked in the previous chapters in this report from the terrestrial to the extraterrestrial domain. To illustrate, biological events that happened more than once on the Earth, such as the evolution of multicellularity (which apparently occurred independently in several different metaphyte and metazoan lineages; Dobzhansky et al., 1977), might be considered as likely accomplishments in the evolutionary developments of other planets. If so, then such events would probably be repeated elsewhere in the universe. Using multicellularity as an example, it would be anticipated that far more Earthlike planets with large multicellular organisms would be found than planets of similar age where evolutionary processes stopped after the production of eukaryotic-like single-celled creatures similar to protozoans. Another example of such an event might be the evolution of image-forming eyes. Complex eyes of the "camera" type (possessing a lens backed by a retina, and equipped with an apparatus for changing and improving the focus) occur in at least two distantly related lineages on the Earth — the cephalopods and the vertebrates. This may be regarded as evidence that they evolved on at least two separate occasions. Similar light-sensing devices that lack an obvious focusing apparatus occur in several other distantly related lineages (worms, snails, and jellyfish, for example) and are often formed from different tissues by different developmental pathways in their respective embryos (Salvini-Plawen and Mayer, 1977). In view of the several distinct instances in which light-sensing organs have arisen in terrestrial organisms, therefore, it seems probable that structures similar to terrestrial eyes are widespread among organisms of any extraterrestrial environment in which sunlight is available. Considerable study and discussion will be required to evaluate the merits of this method of assessment; at present it seems to offer one possibility for making deductions about extra-terrestrial life.

2. Other Worlds, Other Rates of Extraplanetary Disturbance

A second line of approach is suggested by the following question. Could meteorite bombardments at 10 times the rate experienced by the Earth lead to a more rapid development of intelligent life? On Earth, the fossil record may be interpreted to suggest that mammals were prevented from developing a more significant early diversification than that which they actually achieved because of the 130 myr dominance of the planet by reptiles. Suppose, for the moment, that an asteroid like that postulated by the Alvarez team (chapters II and VI) did in fact exterminate the dinosaurs. If so, can that event be regarded as a removal of an evolutionary obstacle (i.e., the dinosaurs), with the result that the mammals were allowed to initiate the developments that ultimately led to the evolution of intelligence? Would repeated impacts by asteroids provide animals with a greater potential for intelligence with an opportunity to develop that potential more quickly? Or would such animals be prevented from flourishing? In other words, is there some "optimum" frequency of large meteorite impact (or other major environmental disturbance) that might accelerate the evolution of intelligent organisms, eventually to prompt their appearance in less time than would be characteristic of comparable situations with higher or lower impact frequencies? And would greater frequencies of disturbance delay this particular evolutionary development, and perhaps increase the probability of some other outcome? Study of this question, coupled with renewed scrutiny of theories of planetary formation, may allow us to identify particular stellar-system environments in which meteorite bombardments are more or less frequent, and in which the rates of evolution of intelligence might be different from that observed on the Earth.

Here, meteor bombardments and intelligence are used as specific examples of an extraplanetary disturbance factor and one form of organic complexity. Similar questions about the origins of other forms of complexity, in connection with other environmental disturbances of extraplanetary origin, can also be explored.

Many of us wondered whether sufficient attention has been paid to "killer factors" capable of exterminating the complex life (or indeed all living things, "simple" or complex) on a planet. Complex terrestrial organisms have been subjected to five episodes of mass extinction, one of which may have exterminated more than 90% of all marine species (chapter III). Episodes capable of 100% extermination would seem to be possible. Supernova explosions, nuclear wars, intense galactic radiation fields, and perhaps even intrinsic biological factors, resulting from poorly understood evolutionary interactions among organisms and their environments, may prove to be more important than is now suspected in eliminating preexisting life from planets. Arguments about the abundance of life in the universe would require modification if such factors are recognized and identified.

The destructive effects of events in space might be expected to exert different effects upon different taxa. A nearby supernova might be expected to raise the level of ionizing radiation at the Earth's surface (in addition to its effects on climate), and a major asteroid impact might be expected to darken the skies and chill the planet (Pollack et al., 1983). The effects on plants, marine organisms, large long-lived organisms, and those of other habitats or ecological niches might well be different in the two cases. Investigation of the expected effects of different extraterrestrial disturbances might improve our ability to determine whether any such events have influenced terrestrial life of the past, to discriminate among the possible events that might have done so, and to visualize broad trends in the evolution of extraterrestrial life on worlds where disturbances of various kinds are more or less frequent.

3. Alternatives to Terrestrial Life Cycles and Historical Patterns

A possible source of inferences about extraterrestrial organisms lies in the study of alternatives to the morphologies and life cycles of terrestrial organisms that we regard as "typical." Bisexual diploidy provides an example here. Although there are many exceptions, "typical" complex terrestrial species are bisexual, and each individual is diploid (that is, possesses two complete coded DNA messages). Many species, however, employ alternative strategies. A few of these are as follows:

(a) Hermaphroditism: each individual is both male and female
(b) Polysexuality: individuals may belong to one of several "sexes"
(c) Polyploidy: each individual carries four or more coded DNA messages
(d) Alternate sexual/asexual reproduction

There are certain disadvantages to bisexual diploidy. For example, a bisexual diploid organism equipped with a particularly favorable combination of genes for life in a certain environment must dismantle that combination and pass randomly selected halves of it to each of its offspring. The offspring are not likely, in this instance, to be as genetically well equipped for life as was their parent. Certain alternative strategies listed above allow their practitioners to sidestep this disadvantage and others associated with bisexual diploidy. On the other hand, they sometimes incur their own disadvantages.

At first glance, some of the alternative strategies seem to be better in terms of adapting organisms to their environments than does bisexual diploidy itself. For example, certain aphids are practitioners of alternate sexual/asexual reproduction. During the summer, all individuals are female and produce identical female offspring for as long as conditions remain favorable. As fall approaches, the females also begin to produce male offspring. Mating occurs, overwintering eggs are laid, and females hatch in the spring to begin the cycle anew. Many plants also combine vegetative (asexual) propagation of offspring with bisexual production of seeds and propagules. In this way, these organisms avail themselves of all of the advantages of purely asexual reproduction, as well as those of bisexual diploidy, while side-stepping some of the disadvantages of both practices.

Why is this "aphid strategy" not more widespread among terrestrial animals? One possible reason may be that, contrary to first impressions, it is not measurably superior to normal practice. Another might be that its superiority, if any can be demonstrated or predicted from theory, is realized only in species with certain restricted habits, morphologies, and generation times. On the other hand, it could be a truly superior genetic strategy that has been late in making its appearance on the Earth for a variety of reasons. It is of fundamental importance to the discussion of extraterrestrial life that these reasons be elucidated through an analysis of the evolutionary pathway that led to bisexual diploidy. The earliest eukaryotic organisms are believed to have been haploid and asexual, yet they gave rise to Phanerozoic lineages of (mostly) complex bisexual organisms with predominantly diploid cells. Could other equally plausible early evolutionary events have guided those earliest eukaryotes directly into a pattern of diploidy with alternating sexual/asexual reproduction? Or is the "aphid strategy" necessarily derivative from other more easily evolved patterns? Should the former be the case, then "typical" organisms of certain other worlds may be endowed from the outset with a genetic strategy that differs from that of "typical" terrestrial organisms. The possibilities for morphological, ecological, and behavioral adaptations, in that event, have hardly been explored, although studies of certain terrestrial organisms might provide preliminary clues. Should the latter be the case, then the relative abundance of this particular derivative genetic system in the galaxy depends upon the time spans available and the plasticities of ancestral systems.

As another example, many higher plants are able to "short circuit" the rather tedious and time-consuming processes of ordinary speciation by a combination of hybridization, anomalous duplication of zygote DNA, and eventual self-fertilization (Stebbins, 1950). The result is that individuals of two separate species may combine their gametes to produce viable fertile offspring of an entirely new species, literally overnight. This practice is not uncommon; the chromosome arrangements of higher plants suggest that approximately 25% of their species arose in this manner. Why is this alternative practice not more widespread on the Earth — and what would be the evolutionary consequences if it were? With the accelerated rate of speciation that this practice permits, would a planet whose organisms typically bud off new species in this manner develop various complex adaptations sooner than one upon which speciation is constrained to operate more slowly?

Similar questions can be asked about other genetic strategies that are employed by certain terrestrial organisms, with a view to assessing the probability of their scarcity or generality among organisms produced by evolutionary scenarios on other worlds.

Theoretical considerations of such questions have hardly been attempted.

Once the ease (or difficulty) of establishment of alternative genetic strategies has been assessed, estimates of the frequency of their occurrence throughout the galaxy may be possible. In certain instances, the implications for complex life are profound. For example, the alternative genetic system of the hymenopteran insects (haploid males, diploid females) is particularly amenable to the evolution of complex social organization (Hamilton, 1964; Wilson, 1971). Complex social organization, in turn, probably constitutes one element of the array of interacting factors that lead to the development of technological civilizations by intelligent species. If studies of the origins of genetic systems suggest that the hymenopteran alternative is able and likely to arise *de novo* in the early millenia of a planet's history (rather than as a late derived alternative to some other system, such as bisexual diploidy, that must evolve first), and is thereby able to establish itself as the "standard" genetic system possessed by all of the planet's subsequent plants and animals, then surprising estimates of the abundance of civilizations in the galaxy may follow.

An intriguing possibility is the prospect that nonmammalian forms may be capable of developing intelligence. Russell and Seguin (1982) have suggested that the relative size of the brain was increasing in certain of the latest dinosaurs, and have envisioned a scenario by which a reptile with intelligence comparable to that of human beings might have evolved. If one need not wait for animals that are closely comparable to mammals in order to anticipate the evolution of intelligence, and if alternative genetic systems that promote the evolution of social cooperation are to be expected elsewhere in the universe, then perhaps intelligent beings could arise more easily than is suggested by the long-delayed appearance of a single intelligent species on Earth. But that possibility, in itself, raises interesting questions. Why did the reptiles fail to evolve intelligence comparable to that of man during their 130 myr dominance of the Earth, while the mammals did so in less than one third of that time, after the dominance of the reptiles ended? At present, little is known of such possibilities. Their study might promote a fuller understanding of the development of intelligence on the Earth and of its nature and abundance elsewhere in the universe.

The foregoing examples, admittedly speculative, illustrate how the study of evolution of terrestrial organisms from a space-oriented perspective might permit tentative inferences about extra-terrestrial life. By examining parallelisms in terrestrial organisms, by asking how these adaptations arose, by asking how the many alternatives to each adaptation were derived, and by determining whether any of those alternatives might themselves become "standard practice" on another planet, we may develop a better sense of the possible differences and similarities to be expected between extraterrestrial life and that of our own planet.

The research recommendations identified by the Workshop members in the preceding chapters provide a significant step in this direction. The most immediate benefit of these studies, of course, would be an improved understanding of the evolutionary biology of the Earth. But an additional benefit, due to the particular focus of this proposed research and that defined in chapter VI (relationships between terrestrial life and events in space) could be an improved ability to identify the spectrum of planetary environments, extraplanetary events, and time spans needed to generate and sustain complex life elsewhere.

C. THE GAIA HYPOTHESIS

It is possible to identify other areas of research that also address the question of extraterrestrial life. One such endeavor — Lovelock's (1979) GAIA hypothesis — was discussed briefly by the Workshop group. Lovelock noted that the terrestrial biosphere has remained at life-supporting temperatures (between $0°$ and about $70°C$) for a period of nearly four billion years, despite a slow and significant increase in the brightness of the Sun. This contrasts dramatically with the severe climatic deteriorations experienced by Mars and Venus. He proposed that living things are responsible for this long-lived climatic stability, and that they evolve in ways that enable them to maintain it. The scientific community is agreed that living things do modify the global environment, often to their own advantage. Thus, it is well known that plants maintain high atmospheric oxygen levels, which in turn give rise to a layer of ozone in the upper atmosphere, which in turn prevents high-energy ultraviolet radiation from reaching the Earth's surface. The development of an atmosphere enriched by oxygen may have made it possible, therefore, for both plants and animals to invade dry land early in Phanerozoic time. If so, this activity of green plants had the effect of improving the habitability of the whole globe for their own descendants and for others. An unproved assertion of this hypothesis is, however, the notion that the biosphere changes in ways that dampen incipient climatic instability. If the Earth were becoming colder, for example, the GAIA hypothesis holds that communities of organisms would tend to modify the atmosphere and oceans with the result that a planetary warming would be initiated, perhaps by a greenhouse effect. This view is disputed by many scientists and its status is currently unresolved. If it were to be shown to be wholly or partially correct, then the implications for abundance of life in the universe would be profound. Rather than regarding life as a phenomenon to be sought on a few atypical planets that happened to experience climatic stability, we would recognize that nearly every planet that produces life would have a better chance of maintaining the climatic and environmental stability needed to sustain its biosphere, possibly through billions of additional years of evolution. Something may be learned about life in the universe, therefore, as well as about evolution and the stability of the climate and of the physical-chemical factors of environments on our own planet by study of this hypothesis. Although many of us are skeptical, we agree that the GAIA mechanism approaches one extreme of a spectrum of possibilities (ranging from total control of a planet's environment by its organisms to total lack of control) and that much further study is needed to determine the causes of large-scale environmental stability and change. The recommendations of other chapters (particularly recommendation 2, chapter IV and recommendations 2 and 3, chapter VI) address this need. The GAIA hypothesis in particular could be investigated by seeking to identify evolutionary mechanisms (if any such exist) that are capable of selecting organisms whose activities promote global environmental stability.

D. IDENTIFICATION OF SUITABLE PLANETARY ENVIRONMENTS

Yet another avenue of approach to questions about extraterrestrial life involves theoretical efforts to identify planetary environments within which life might develop complexity. Two of the recommendations of this report bear upon the environmental limits that life is able to tolerate, and constraints, imposed by mechanics, gravity, available or potential organic materials and the basic needs of living systems, to the forms that life can assume. This research may reveal whether living things, perhaps of alternative biochemistries and construction, can occupy environmental conditions that are mildly or dramatically different from those known to exist on the Earth. A complementary study, using knowledge that is already available and information that may be forthcoming from this research, can be initiated to identify those alternative environments. Research by NASA and other institutions has generally broadened our view of the sorts of planets that might be suitable for occupancy by life. It now seems conceivable, for example, that a satellite of a gaseous giant planet might serve as a site for the origin of simple anaerobic life and for subsequent evolution of more complex forms. Different satellites of Jupiter are now known to possess water ice and perhaps liquid water, warmth generated by tidal interactions, and adequate sunlight for positive net photosynthesis. Theoretical work is needed to reveal the circumstances under which a single satellite might possess all of these, as well as the other properties needed to generate and sustain complex life. Such a satellite has been envisioned in a scenario by Hartmann et al. (1982) (see frontispiece to this chapter); if such can be shown to be physically compatible with inhabitation by complex organisms, then we may expand our search for complex life to greater distances from parent stars than have been considered previously.

In addition to the better definition of planets that are suitable for life, better identification of their locales in space can now be attempted. As one possibility, space scientists are moving toward a new view that stable planetary orbits are possible near the stars of multiple systems (Harrington, 1981). Study of the likelihood that planets will actually form and settle into stable orbits during the formation of such systems is now needed, as are determinations of the kinds of conditions that would occur on their surfaces. If the presence of a major and a minor "sun," the semi-erratic long- and short-term changes in daylengths and seasons, the confused tides and other environmental factors on such a world seem to permit the origin and development of complex life, then the possibilities for seeking life in the universe are expanded by perhaps as much as a factor of 10, since approximately 85% of all stars are in multiple systems (Allen, 1973). The search for life-bearing locales can also be expanded by consideration of late spectral-type main-sequence stars (for example, M-dwarfs) as candidates for life. A prevalent view is that these small dim stars emit too little ultraviolet light to catalyze the origin of life on their planets, that their tendency to flare violently might create lethal conditions on nearby planets, and that the neighborhoods in which planets could possess liquid water are too narrow and close to the star to be likely to contain planets (Goldsmith and Owen, 1980). It is not known whether planets would form at great distances from such small stars, or at distances more conducive to the development of complex life. The latter would be the case if Bode's law (an empirical formula that expresses the relationship between the radii of the orbits of the planets) proves to be applicable to planetary systems in general.

New knowledge of environments on the satellites of dark "Jovian" companions, mentioned earlier, raises other possibilities for the presence of life near M-dwarf stars. In addition, such stars have immense lifetimes, and those formed at any time after the cosmic increase in abundance of the biogenic elements are still in their main-sequence phase of activity today. Such stars can live for twice as long as the Sun, providing many billions of years for the development of simple and complex life in their vicinities. If some combination of conditions permits life-bearing planets to exist near such stars, then the search for life can again be expanded many times, due to the great abundance of such stars.

E. INTELLIGENT LIFE IN THE UNIVERSE

One of the most fascinating possibilities in any consideration of complex extraterrestrial life is that certain extraterrestrial species may be possessed of intelligence comparable to that of human beings. This raises questions that may be placed in two categories.

First, what are the conditions under which intelligence — that is, mental and manipulative abilities comparable to those of humans — may develop? Must a complex organism have a brain in excess of some threshold mass in order to develop intelligence? Can a neural organ of some alternative design develop comparable abilities in a smaller space? Can intelligent technological beings evolve underwater? Are certain animal forms (e.g., specialized ones, as for flight) somehow prohibited from also developing intelligence? Can two intelligent species evolve simultaneously and coexist? Many similar questions can be asked about the ways in which organisms and environments interact to result eventually in the evolution of intelligent beings.

Questions of a second category deal with observable activities of intelligent beings in the universe. For example, have intelligent beings elsewhere in the universe generated electromagnetic signals, either deliberately or by leakage from transmitter systems, that can be detected on the Earth? Other questions could be phrased to address the extent to which intelligent beings have influenced the nature and distribution of complex life in the universe, for example by transporting living things to planets that were originally lifeless. Except for the possibility of intercepting electromagnetic transmissions, we have no means of evaluating such questions at present.

Although the evolution of intelligence was sometimes discussed as an example of the development of one type of complexity in living things, we made no special effort to isolate this important aspect of planetary biology or to give it special consideration, since our major concern was the variety of other forms of complexity developed over Phanerozoic time. We feel that intelligence may merit attention as a separate issue, perhaps comparable in importance to the study of complex life as a whole, addressed here. Our last proposed research recommendation suggests a way of beginning this task.

F. RESEARCH RECOMMENDATIONS

Our consensus was that the questions outlined in the previous chapters are those upon which the majority of the proposed research effort should be concentrated. Many bear directly and indirectly upon questions about extraterrestrial life. Other recommendations, phrased as questions whose answers should be sought, are listed below. The result of continued efforts in these areas will be a better understanding of life on our own planet and, sometime in the future, when targets for interstellar life-detecting probes are being considered, a better understanding of where to send them and what to look for.

Recommendation 1

Is the evolution of complexity inevitable, given that eukaryote-like cells are available, in planetary environments that are similar to (and dissimilar from) those of the early Earth? (This question is also addressed by recommendation 2 of chapter III).

Recommendation 2

What are the relationships between the rates and types of disturbances of life by events in Space, and the rates and directions of the evolution of complex life? How might extraplanetary disturbances influence evolution elsewhere in the universe, where their rates and relative severities may differ from those in the present and past neighborhoods of the solar system? (These questions are partially addressed by recommendation 4 of chapter III and recommendations 1 and 4 of chapter VI).

Recommendation 3

Have terrestrial organisms evolved in ways that cause their activities to counteract detrimental climatic and environmental changes on the Earth's surface? Is there reason to believe that they might (or might not) do so elsewhere? (This question is addressed, in part, by recommendation 2 of chapter IV).

Recommendation 4

What evolutionary events and processes were responsible for the fact that bisexual diploidy is prevalent among terrestrial animals? How was the hymenopteran alternative derived from bisexual diploidy? Is it likely, or possible, that early events and processes could give rise to the hymenopteran alternative directly, or to other alternatives to bisexual diploidy?

Recommendation 5

What combinations of physical, chemical, and planetary characteristics can make a planet or satellite capable of sustaining complex life? Where (with respect to star type, distance from the parent star, and location in the galaxy) are life-sustaining planets likely to be found? Are certain of these planets more or less vulnerable to disturbances by events in space? Are the circumstances of their formation such that they are more or less likely to experience disturbances from sources in space than is the Earth? (Effects of a planet's orientation with respect to its star, its orbital properties, and its relationship with a satellite are addressed by recommendation 2 of chapter VI).

Recommendation 6

Can life-sustaining conditions (such as those identified by recommendation 5 above) occur on the planets of multiple star systems, on bodies orbiting M-dwarf stars or their companions? Is the formation of such planets probable?

Recommendation 7

Can we identify factors in the emergence of human intelligence on the Earth that seem to be specific to the particular history of our planet, and factors that might be expected to influence the evolution of human-like intelligence on planets with other environments and other evolutionary histories?

GLOSSARY

Acoelomate. See "Coelomate."

Acritarch. A microfossil of uncertain relationship to existing and fossil organisms, perhaps a unicellular alga. Mostly organic in composition. Especially common in Precambrian time; these may be the oldest known eukaryotic cells.

Allele. See "Gene."

Angiosperm. A plant that forms seeds in structures that develop from flowers. Flowering seed plants, the most sophisticated of living plants, in their anatomy and life cycle. Grasses, palms, broadleaf trees, flowering shrubs, etc.

Ångström. A unit of measure, used with reference to wavelengths of light. One Angstrom = 10^{-10} m = 10^{-4} μ.

Annelids, Annelida (phylum). Worms whose body plans include division of the body into similar segments and other characteristic-shared features. Earthworms, leeches, many marine worms ("polychaetes").

Arborescence. Refers to a tree-like growth form or shape.

Archaean Eon. See "TIME," Item 1.

Archaeocyatha (phylum). Vase-shaped, immobile calcareous organisms that evolved, then became extinct, during the Cambrian period. Traditionally considered to be sponge-like animals but may, in fact, be algal.

Arthropods, Arthropoda (phylum). Animals with jointed legs, external skeletons, and segmented bodies. Crustaceans, spiders, insects, centipedes, trilobites, and others. A huge assemblage of animals, dominant on the modern Earth and in ancient times.

Banded-Iron Formation. Alternating layers of reduced and oxidized iron minerals, largely formed about 2 byr ago, that give evidence of the initial stages of introduction of oxygen to the Earth's atmosphere.

Benthic. Refers to the bottom of the sea (or fresh waters). Benthic organisms are those that live on or in the bottom; the benthic environment is that at the bottom, etc.

Brachiopods, Brachiopoda (phylum). Bivalved shellfish, superficially similar to clams, but fundamentally different in their anatomies. Articulate brachiopods are those whose two shells articulate to form a strong hinge joint; inarticulate brachiopods are those whose shells do not meet to form a hinge. Brachiopods were much more prominent members of marine communities in ancient times than they are today; they are important index fossils.

Cambrian period. See "TIME," Item 7.

Carboniferous period. See "TIME," Item 11.

Cenozoic era. See "TIME," Item 6.

Cephalopods, Cephalopoda. Squids, octopuses, nautiluses, cuttlefish, and their extinct shell-bearing relatives. A class of the Mollusc phylum.

Chromosomes. Elongated molecules that carry the genetic material, occurring in the nuclei of eukaryotic cells. See "diploid."

Chordates, Chordata (phylum). Animals whose body plans contain dorsal nerve cords, gill slits, and other shared features. The phylum is divided into three groups; a number of obscure

162

marine invertebrates and the spectacularly advanced and successful vertebrate animals.

Clade. All of the organisms whose ancestry can be traced to one particular species living at an earlier time. Therefore, a group of all related species.

Cnidaria (phylum). Jellyfish, corals, sea anemones and related living and extinct animals, all of which share a basic body plan. Pronounced "ni-dare'-i-a."

Coelomate. An animal is "coelomate" if it possesses a hollow, nondigestive, nonrespiratory space in the interior of its body (a "coelom") that is formed in a particular way. An advanced and complex feature with many advantages, found in all higher animals (and modified to different degrees). Pronounced "Seel'-o-mate." Acoelomate: not coelomate, with no such hollow interior space. Eucoelomate: coelomate animals whose coeloms develop in the most advanced manner now known.

Cretaceous period. See "TIME," Item 15.

Cretaceous-Tertiary boundary event. A general term to describe the unusually high observed rates of extinction at or near the Cretaceous-Tertiary boundary (approximately 66 myr ago), and its possible biotic and abiotic causal mechanisms.

Crinoids. Relatives of starfish. Crinoids resemble feathery stars; they may be permanently attached to the sea bottom by a stalk, or free-living. Formerly more abundant than they are at present. A class of the Echinoderm phylum.

Cyanobacteria. Bacteria (sometimes called "blue-green algae") whose photosynthesis liberates oxygen. Cyanobacteria first appeared sometime between about 2.2 and 3.5 byr ago; their activities added oxygen to the atmosphere and created stony reefs ("stromatolites").

Detritivores. Organisms that live by eating loose edible muck ("detritus") on the sea bottom. Sea cucumbers, certain clams and worms, etc.

Devonian period. See "TIME," Item 10.

Diploid. Refers to a cell whose nucleus contains two complete sets of chromosomes. Diploid cells occur in most complex plants and animals; the two sets are copies of single sets, each of which was contributed to that organism by one of its parents. Diploidy: having diploid cells. An advanced feature. See "haploid."

Echinoderms, Echinodermata (phylum). Marine animals with more or less plated exterior surfaces, peculiar internal hydraulic systems, and other shared anatomical attributes. Starfish, sea urchins (echinoids), brittle stars, sea cucumbers, crinoids, and many related forms that are now extinct.

Echinoids. See Echinoderms.

Ecliptic. The plane in space defined by the orbit of the Earth.

Ediacarian interval. See "TIME," Item 26.

Eocene epoch. See "TIME," Item 19.

Epifauna. Those animals that live on the sea bottom (as opposed to those that burrow into the bottom, the "infauna"). Many crabs, snails, trilobites, brachiopods, sponges, etc.

Epigenetic. Refers to successive changes in the shape and structure of a developing embryo imposed upon it by the actions of its genes interacting with external stimuli.

Eucoelomate. See "Coelomate."

Eukaryotic. Refers to cells whose internal construction is complex, consisting of organelles (e.g., nucleus, mitochondria, etc.), chromosomes, and other structures. All higher organisms are built of eukaryotic cells, as are many single-celled organisms (protists). The evolution of complex life apparently had to await the evolution of eukaryotic cells, an event that occurred about 1 byr ago. Eukaryote: an organism built of

164

eukaryotic cells. See "prokaryotic." Pronounced "you'-carry-otic."

Extant. Refers to organisms of taxa that are living today, as opposed to "extinct," organisms of taxa that have no living representatives.

Extinction. The elimination or disappearance of all of the organisms of a taxon. Extinction may refer to a single species, a group of species, or higher taxa consisting of few or many species.

Foraminifera. Single-celled marine organisms ("protoctists") that produce small shells. They may be pelagic or benthic. The accumulation of foram shells on the sea bottom is of crucial significance to interpretation of Mesozoic and Cenozoic climates and other properties of the Earth.

Form genus (plural: form genera). A list or category of organisms whose parts resemble each other in many of their minute details. The organisms may or may not be closely related by descent. Form genera are categories used by paleobiologists who are unable to find enough of the fossilized organisms to determine their true evolutionary relationships. Some pollen grains and leaves, for example, are placed in form genera.

GAIA hypothesis. The conjecture that organisms evolve in such a way that their activities counteract incipient global environmental deterioration and maintain the habitability of the planet in defiance of abiotic and astrophysical events that would otherwise degrade it.

Gastropods. Snails, limpets, sea slugs and related animals, characterized by possession of a muscular creeping foot, a ribbon-like feeding apparatus (the "radula"), a single shell, and other anatomical similarities. A class of the phylum Mollusca.

Gene. A unit of biological "information." Physically, a gene is a small sector of a DNA molecule. Each gene contributes to the pattern of growth, the appearance, and the day-to-day activity of the organism that possesses it. Alternative versions of a particular gene (say, that for eye color) may cause it to operate differently in different individuals (red eyes in one, white eyes in another, etc.) Each alternative is called an "allele."

Genome. All of the genes carried by a single gamete. In some usages, the total chromosome or gene content of a cell nucleus. In the latter case, the entire genetic complement of an organism.

Genotype. All or part of the genetic makeup of a particular individual. A list of some (or all) of its genes.

Gymnosperm. A plant that forms seeds in structures that do not develop from flowers. Nonflowering seed plants (e.g., conifers, cycads).

Haploid. Refers to a cell whose nucleus contains one complete set of chromosomes. Haploid cells are usually gametes, but some complex plants and animals are composed entirely of haploid cells. Fusion of gametes produces a single diploid cell, the duplication of which (with other processes) forms a diploid organism. See "diploid."

Hemichordates, Hemichordata (phylum). Worms whose body plans and early development show suggestive traces of a distant relationship with the chordate phylum. Not common at present.

Heterospory. Refers to plants that produce spores of two different sizes; each develops into a unisexual (male or female) gametophyte. Heterospory is regarded as an advanced evolutionary condition.

Hymenoptera. Bees, wasps, ants, and related insects. In addition to their anatomical similarities, they possess a genetic system that is apparently conducive to social cooperation and organization. An order of the Class Insecta.

166

Hyolithida, hyolithids. Small tapering subcylindrical shells with opercula (lids) that occur as fossils from the Cambrian to the Permian period. Their relationship to other phyla is uncertain.

Infauna. Those animals that burrow into the sea bottom (as opposed to those that live on the bottom, the "epifauna"). Worms, clams, etc.

Jurassic period. See "TIME," Item 14.

Karyotypic. Refers to the physical dimensions and appearance of an organism's chromosomes.

Mass extinction. An unusually severe extinction event, occurring in a relatively short time compared with normal "background" extinction rates of the affected taxa. Mass extinction usually involves the extermination of higher taxa (orders and families).

Mesozoic era. See "TIME," Item 5.

Metaphytes. Multicellular plants composed of cells that are differentiated into several distinct types, and whose activities are tightly coordinated; that is, complex plants. See "Metazoa," the comparable term for animals.

Metazoa, Metazoans. Multicellular animals composed of cells that are differentiated into several distinct types, and whose activities are tightly coordinated; that is, complex animals. As opposed to protozoans (or "protoctists"), organisms that are either unicellular or composed of many similar cells whose activities are not tightly coordinated).

Miocene epoch. See "TIME," Item 21.

Morphogenesis. The process by which a developing embryo assumes the proper shape and internal construction (i.e., the morphology) of organisms of its particular species.

Multicellular. Refers to any organism whose body is composed of a large number of cells whose metabolic activities are coordinated.

Neogene interval. See "TIME," Item 29.

Oligocene epoch. See "TIME," Item 20.

Ordovician period. See "TIME," Item 8.

Ostracods. Small marine crustaceans whose heavy bivalved shells are abundant as fossils and useful as indicators of environmental conditions of the past.

Paleocene epoch. See "TIME," Item 18.

Paleogene interval. See "TIME," Item 28.

Paleozoic era. See "TIME," Item 4.

Parenchyma. Cells capable of division in all three directions, or connected to all adjoining cells.

Pelagic. Refers to the water that is not in close contact with the bottom of the sea. Pelagic animals are those found up and off the sea bottom (fish, for example), the pelagic realm is the mid-water environment, etc. Usually refers to waters far from shore.

Permian period. See "TIME," Item 12.

Phanerozoic eon. See "TIME," Item 3.

Phylum. A category (or group or list) of those animals that share a similar basic body plan which differs significantly from the body plans of all other animals. Example: the animals of the phylum Cnidaria all possess stinging cells, radial symmetry, bodies composed of two layers of cells, and no anus, a combination not seen in other animals. Plural "phyla." All animals are classified into phyla. Each phylum is subdivided into smaller categories (classes) which are further subdivided. Shown in table III-1.

Pleistocene epoch. See "TIME," Item 23.

168

Pliocene epoch. See "TIME," Item 22.

Polymorphism. The condition whereby the shapes and/or colors of different individuals may be distinctly different, even though they are all members of the same species. Example: snails of one species whose shells are coiled either in a left-handed or a right-handed manner exhibit polymorphism. Literally: many shapes.

Precambrian interval. See "TIME," Item 24.

Priapulids, Priapulida (phylum). Worms with a distinctive body plan; only a few obscure species exist today.

Prokaryotic. A term that describes cells whose internal construction and activities are relatively simple. Such cells lack organelles, chromosomes, and other complex internal units. Prokaryote — an organism built of one or more prokaryotic cells; mainly bacteria and cyanobacteria. Most prokaryotes are single-celled organisms, or consist of simple filaments or sheets of cells. Eukaryotic cells evolved from prokaryotes.

Proterozoic era. See "TIME," Item 2.

Pseudoextinction. Disappearance of a species via its transformation or evolution into some new descendant species. Pseudoextinction is distinguished from true extinction, in which a species disappears without leaving any living descendants.

Pseudoparenchyma. Aggregated filaments, occurring in some algae, that resemble the "parenchyma" (specialized and other cells) of complex or "higher" plants.

Pteridophyte. Any complex land plant that reproduces by means of spores and exhibits a life cycle that involves alternation of haploid and diploid generations. Ferns, club mosses, horsetails. Pronounced "ter-id'-o-phyte."

Quaternary period. See "TIME," Item 17.

Random drift. A change in the relative abundance of any particular genetic trait in a population, from generation to generation, that arises as a result of random processes (e.g., the vagaries of mate selection or chromosome recombination), rather than from natural selective processes.

Rhyniophytes. Early complex plants; small, lacking true leaves and roots, consisting mostly of forked axes with terminal spore-bearing bodies, existing during the Silurian and Devonian periods.

Silurian period. See "TIME," Item 9.

Speciation. The process whereby a single existing species gives rise to one or more new species over a period of time.

Species. In everyday language, a "kind" of organism. By one definition, all of the organisms that are capable of interbreeding with each other (under "natural" conditions) to produce fertile offspring (bisexual organisms) or all of the morphologically and genetically similar descendants of some inferred ancestral individual (asexual organisms).

Speciose. Refers to a restricted group of organisms that is characterized by a great number of closely related living species. Example: the speciose genus *Sebastes,* a Pacific rock fish with about 60 very similar and closely related species.

Stasis. A condition whereby directional evolution seems to cease; organisms retain their forms for very long periods without directional change. An evolutionary equilibrium.

Stromatolite. A layered (usually rocky) formation, sometimes reaching the size of a reef, created by the activities of simple organisms (usually cyanobacteria). Common in Precambrian time, much rarer today.

Taxonomic groups. Categories into which organisms are classified, for ease in discussion and for portrayal of evolutionary relationships. Taxon: one such category, whether large and inclusive or small and exclusive. Plural, taxa. The taxa are shown and named in table III-1.

Tertiary period. See "TIME," Item 16.

TIME. Most of the TIME intervals described below are shown in figure III-1, or on the inner front cover of this report. After Palmer (1983).

The Eons

Item
1. **Archaean eon.** The 1-byr interval preceding the Proterozoic eon. Spans the time from 3.8 to 2.5 byr ago, during which life originated and simple prokaryotic organisms proliferated.

2. **Proterozoic eon.** The 2-byr interval preceding the Phanerozoic eon. Spans the time from 2.5 to 0.57 byr ago, during which single-celled organisms acquired bisexuality, diploidy, and multicellularity, the biological starting points from which complex life evolved.

3. **Phanerozoic eon.** The last 570 myr of Earth's history, spanning the entire time for which fossils are abundant. The Phanerozoic eon is subdivided into three long eras of unequal length (items 4–6) and eleven relatively short periods (items 7–17).

The Eras

4. **Paleozoic era.** The first 325 myr of the Phanerozoic eon. The Paleozoic era is subdivided into six shorter periods (items 7–12). Characterized by expansions and extinctions of early archaic plants and animals, and terminated by the Permian mass extinction.

5. **Mesozoic era.** A 179-myr subdivision of the Phanerozoic eon. Follows the first subdivision (Paleozoic era) and is itself subdivided into three shorter periods (items 13–15). Characterized by the rise and fall of dinosaurs; the Age of Reptiles.

171

Item

6. **Cenozoic era.** The last 66 myr of the Phanerozoic eon. The Cenozoic is subdivided into two unequal periods (items 16 and 17, Tertiary and Quaternary, which are themselves further subdivided). Characterized by the evolutionary radiation of mammals; the Age of Mammals.

The Periods

7. **Cambrian period.** First period of the Phanerozoic eon. Main biological events include the first widespread appearance of organisms with skeletons, final stages of the major diversification begun in Precambrian time, several episodes of extinction. Duration: approximately 65 myr.

8. **Ordovician period.** Second period of the Phanerozoic eon. Main biological events include the origin and expansion of many invertebrate classes, first vertebrates, and a mass extinction episode. Life mostly marine. Duration: approximately 67 myr.

9. **Silurian period.** Third period of the Phanerozoic eon. The main biological event was the invasion of land by plants. Duration: approximately 30 myr.

10. **Devonian period.** Fourth period of the Phanerozoic eon. Main biological events include the invasion of land by vertebrates; first amphibians; major diversification of fish; a mass extinction episode. Duration: approximately 48 myr.

11. **Carboniferous period.** Fifth period of the Phanerozoic eon. Main biological events include the first reptiles and coal-forming jungles of fernlike plants. Duration: approximately 74 myr.

12. **Permian period.** Sixth period of the Phanerozoic eon. The main biological event was the most severe mass extinction in Earth's history. Duration: approximately 41 myr.

Item

13. **Triassic period.** Seventh period of the Phanerozoic eon. Main biological events include the first conifer-like plants, and the first dinosaurs and mammals. Duration: approximately 37 myr.

14. **Jurassic period.** Eighth period of the Phanerozoic eon. Main biological events include the first birds and flourishing dinosaurs. Duration: approximately 64 myr.

15. **Cretaceous period.** Ninth period of the Phanerozoic eon. Main biological events include the first flowering plants, big radiation of fishes, and a mass extinction episode resulting in the disappearance of dinosaurs. Duration: approximately 78 myr.

16. **Tertiary period.** Tenth period of the Phanerozoic eon. Main biological events include widespread radiation of mammals, birds, flowering plants, insects. Duration: approximately 65 myr. This period is subdivided in several ways; see Items 18–22, 28–29.

17. **Quaternary period.** Eleventh and last period of the Phanerozoic eon. Main biological events include the modernization of human beings and widespread extinction of land mammals. Duration: approximately 2 myr.

The Epochs

18. **Paleocene epoch.** First subdivision of the Tertiary period. A time when complex life was recovering from the mass extinction of the preceding Cretaceous period. Duration: approximately 8.6 myr.

19. **Eocene epoch.** Second subdivision of the Tertiary period. Major evolutionary changes occurred in mammals. Terminated by an extinction episode of moderate proportions. Duration: approximately 21.2 myr.

Item

20. **Oligocene epoch.** Third subdivision of the Tertiary period. Evolutionary changes occurred among mammals, following an extinction episode that terminated the preceding Eocene epoch. Duration: approximately 12.9 myr.

21. **Miocene epoch.** Fourth subdivision of the Tertiary period. A time of maximum mammal size and diversity. Duration: approximately 18.4 myr.

22. **Pliocene epoch.** Fifth subdivision of the Tertiary period. A time characterized by the appearance of hominids and by great mammal diversity. Duration: approximately 3.7 myr.

23. **Pleistocene epoch.** First subdivision of the Quaternary period, characterized by the modernization of human beings, extinctions of large land mammals, and the most recent Ice Age. Duration: approximately 1.6 myr.

Other Intervals

24. **Precambrian.** All of the time preceding the Phanerozoic eon (whose first subdivision is the Cambrian period). Duration: 4 byr.

25. **Vendian.** The interval immediately preceding the Phanerozoic. Main biological events include the rapid evolution of the major body plans of the animal phyla and the earliest traceable (and most important) changes in organism complexity in Earth's history. Duration: about 120 myr.

26. **Ediacarian.** An interval immediately preceding the Phanerozoic eon, during which soft-bodied marine organisms left poorly preserved fossils. The Ediacarian interval is included within the slightly longer Vendian interval; we have used the term Vendian throughout this report.

TIME (concluded)

Item

    27. **Tommotian.** The 20-myr interval (or stage) between latest Vendian and earliest Precambrian time. Assigned to the Cambrian period in some works, considered as latest Vendian time in others.

    28. **Paleogene.** The span of time that encompasses the early Tertiary period, or the Paleocene, Oligocene, and Eocene epochs. The first 43 myr of the Cenozoic era.

    29. **Neogene.** The span of time that encompasses the later Tertiary period, or the Miocene and Pliocene epochs. Duration: 22 myr.

Tommotian interval. See "TIME," Item 27.

Tracheophyte. Any plant that contains elongated hollow cells arranged in a system of internal water-conducting tubes or pipes. All complex plants; ferns and conifers and their respective relatives, and flowering plants.

Triassic period. See "TIME," Item 13.

Vendian interval. See "TIME," Item 25.

Zone (stratigraphic). Any stratum or body of strata characterized by a fossil taxon (or taxa) from which it takes its name. Zones delineate the "fine structure" of larger strata.

Zosterophyllophytes. Early complex plants, consisting of unequally branched axes with lateral spore-bearing bodies, lacking true roots and leaves, from the Devonian period.

REFERENCES

Allen, Clabon W.: Astrophysical Quantities. Third ed. Athlone Press, Univ. of London, 1973.

Alvarez, L. W.; Alvarez, W.; Asaro, F.; and Michel, H. V.: Extraterrestrial Cause for the Cretaceous-Tertiary Extinction. Science, vol. 208, 1980, pp. 1095–1108.

Alvarez, Walter; Asaro, Frank; Michel, Helen V.; and Alvarez, Luis: Iridium Anomaly Approximately Synchronous with Terminal Eocene Extinctions. Science, vol. 216, 1982, pp. 886–888.

Archibald, J. David; and Clemens, William A.: Late Cretaceous Extinctions. Amer Sci., vol. 70, no. 4, 1982, pp. 377–385.

Asimov, Isaac: A Choice of Catastrophes. Simon and Schuster, New York, 1979, pp. 115–119.

Bambach, R. K.: Species Richness in Marine Benthic Habitats through the Phanerozoic. Paleobiology, vol. 30, no. 2, 1977, pp. 152–167.

Bambach, R. K.: Ecospace Utilization and Guilds in Marine Communities Through the Phanerozoic. Biotic Interactions in Recent and Fossil Benthic Communities, M. J. O. Tevesz and P. L. McCall, eds. Plenum Publ. Co., New York, 1983.

Bambach, Richard K.; Scotese, Christopher R.; and Zeigler, Alfred M.: Before Pangea: the Geographies of the Paleozoic World. Amer. Sci., vol. 68, 1980, pp. 26–38.

Barron, E. J.; Harrison, C. G. A.; Sloan, S. L., III; and Hay, W. W.: Paleogeography, 180 Million Years to the Present. Eclogae geol. Helvet., vol. 74, part II, 1981, pp. 443–470.

Benson, R. H.: In Search of Lost Oceans: a Paradox in Discovery. Historical Biogeography, J. Grey and A. Boucot, eds. Univ. Oregon Press, 1979, pp. 375–390; also in Proceedings of the 37th Biology Colloquium and Selected Papers, pp. 379–389.

Berkner, L. V.; and Marshall, L. C.: On the Origin and Rise of Oxygen Concentration in the Earth's Atmosphere. Jour. Atmos. Sci., vol. 22, 1965, pp. 225–261.

Berry, W. B.; and P. Wilde: Progressive Ventilation of the Oceans — an Explanation for the Distribution of Lower Paleozoic Black Shales. Amer. Jour. Sci., vol. 278, no. 3, 1978, pp. 257–275.

Billingham, J., ed.: Life in the Universe. MIT Press, Cambridge, Mass., 1981.

Bolin, B.; Degens, E. T.; Kempe, S.; and Ketner, R., eds.: Workshop on the Carbon Cycle, Ratzeburg, Germany, 1977. The Global Carbon Cycle. J. Wiley, New York, 1979. (Scope report B.)

Brandt, J. C.; Stephen, T. P.; Crawford, D. C.; and Maran, S. P.: The Gum Nebula: Fossil Stromgren Sphere of the Vela X Supernova. Ap. J., vol. 163, 1971, pp. 99–104.

Brasier, M. D.: The Cambrian Radiation Event. Syst. Assoc., spec. vol. 12, 1979, pp. 103–159.

Bray, J. R.: Pleistocene Volcanism and Glacial Initiation. Science, vol. 197, 1977, pp. 251–254.

Brouwer, Dirk; and Van Woerkom, A. J. J.: The Secular Variations of the Orbital Elements of the Principal Planets. Astronomical papers prepared for the use of the American Ephemeris and Nautical Almanac, vol. 13, no. 2, U.S. Govt. Printing Office, 1950, pp. 81–107.

Budyko, Mikhail I.: Climatic Changes. Amer. Geophys. Union, Washington, D.C., 1977.

Cisne, J. L.: Evolution of the World Fauna of Aquatic Free-Living Arthropods. Evolution, vol. 28, no. 3, 1974, pp. 337–366.

Clark, David H.: Superstars. J. M. Dent and Sons, London, 1979.

Claypool, G. E.; Holser, W. T.; Kaplan, I. R.; Saki, H.; and Zak, I.: The Age Curves of Sulfur and Oxygen Isotopes in Marine Sulfate and Their Mutual Interpretation. Chem. Geol., vol. 28, 1980, pp. 199–260.

Clemmey, H.; and Badham, N.: Oxygen in the Precambrian Atmosphere; an Evaluation of the Geological Evidence. Geology, vol. 10, no. 3, 1982, pp. 141–146.

Cloud, P.: Beginnings of Biospheric Evolution and the Biochemical Consequences. Paleobiology, vol. 2, no. 4, 1976, pp. 351–387.

Cloud, Preston; and Glaessner, Martin F.: The Ediacarian Period and System: Metazoa Inherit the Earth. Science, vol. 217, 1982, pp. 783–792.

Conway Morris, S.: Burgess Shale. The Encyclopedia of Paleontology, R. W. Fairbridge and D. Jablonski, eds., Dowden, Hutchinson and Ross, Stroudsburg, Pa., 1979a, pp. 153–160.

Conway Morris, S.: The Burgess Shale (Middle Cambrian) Fauna. Ann. Rev. Ecol. Syst., vol. 10, 1979b, pp. 327–349.

Cowie, J. W.; and Cribb, S. J.: The Cambrian System. The Geologic Time Scale, G. V. Cohee, M. F. Glaessner, and H. J. Hedberg, eds., Studies in Geology, No. 6. Amer. Assoc. Petrol. Geol., 1978, pp. 355–362.

Crowell, John C.; and Frakes, Lawrence A.: Phanerozoic Glaciation and the Causes of Ice Ages. Amer. Jour. Sci., vol. 268, 1970, pp. 193–224.

Darwin, Charles: On the Origin of Species by Means of Natural Selection. John Murray, London, 1859.

Darwin, G. H.: On the Secular Change in the Elements of the Orbit of a Satellite Revolving About a Tidally Distorted Planet. Phil. Trans. Roy. Soc. London, vol. 171, 1880, pp. 713-891.

Davis, R., Jr.; and Evans, J. C., Jr.: Neutrinos From the Sun. The New Solar Physics, John A. Eddy, ed., Westview Press, for the American Association for the Advancement of Science, Washington, D.C., 1978, pp. 35-57.

Dewey, John P.; and Bird, John M.: Mountain Belts and the New Global Tectonics. Jour. Geophys. Res., vol. 75, 1970, pp. 2625-2647.

Dilke, F. W. W.; and Gough, D. O.: The Solar Spoon, Nature, vol. 240, 1972, pp. 262-264, 293-294.

Dobzhansky, T. G.; Ayala, F. J.; Stebbins, G. L.; and Valentine, J. W.: Evolution, Freeman, San Francisco, Calif., 1977.

Donn, W. L.; and Shaw, D. M.: Model of Climate Evolution Based on Continental Drift and Polar Wandering, Bull., Geol. Soc. Am., vol. 88, 1977, pp. 390-396.

Douglas, R. G.; and Savin, S. M.: Oxygen and Carbon Isotope Analyses of Tertiary and Cretaceous Microfossils from Shatsky Rise and Other Sites in the North Pacific Ocean. Initial Reports of the Deep Sea Drilling Project, vol. 32, 1975, pp. 509-520.

Eddy, J. A.: The Historical Record of Solar Activity. The Ancient Sun, R. O. Pepin, J. A. Eddy, and R. B. Merrill, eds. Pergamon Press, New York, 1980, pp. 119-134.

Eldredge, Niles; and Gould, Stephen Jay: Punctuated Equilibria: an Alternative to Phyletic Gradualism. Models in Paleobiology, Thomas J. M. Schopf, ed. Freeman, Cooper and Co., San Francisco, 1972, pp. 82-115.

Eldredge, Niles; and Cracraft, J.: Phylogenetic Patterns and the Evolutionary Process. Columbia Univ. Press, N.Y., 1980.

Emiliani, Cesare: The Cause of the Ice Ages. Earth and Planet. Sci. Lett., vol. 37, 1978, pp. 349-352.

Emiliani, Cesare; Kraus, Eric B.; and Shoemaker, Eugene M.: Sudden Death at the End of the Mesozoic. Earth and Planet. Sci. Lett., vol. 55, 1981, pp. 317-334.

Ewing, Maurice; and Donn, William L.. A Theory of the Ice Ages. Science, vol. 123, 1956, pp. 1061-1066.

Fenton, Carroll L.; and Fenton, M. A.: The Fossil Book. Doubleday & Co., Inc., Garden City, New York, 1958.

Fischer, A.: G. Gilbert. Bedding Rhythms and Geochronology. The Scientific Ideas of G. K. Gilbert, an Assessment on the Occasion of the Centennial of the United States Geological Survey (1879-1979), E. Yochelson, ed. Geol. Soc. Amer. Spec. Paper 183, 1980, pp. 93-104.

Fischer, A.: Climatic Oscillations in the Biosphere. Biotic Crises in Ecological and Evolutionary Time, Matthew H. Nitecki, ed. Proceedings of the Spring Systematic Symposium, Third ed., Field Museum of Natural History, Academic Press, New York, 1981, pp. 103-131.

Fischer, A.: Long-Term Climatic Oscillations Recorded in Stratigraphy. Climate in Earth History, Studies in Geophysics. Nat. Academy Press, 1982, pp. 97-104.

Fischer, A. G.; and Arthur, M. A.: Secular Variations in the Pelagic Realm. Deep Water Carbonate Environments, H. E. Cook and P. Enos, eds., Spec. Publ. Soc. Econ. Paleontol. and Mineral., no. 25, 1977, pp. 19-50.

Flint, Richard F.: Glacial and Quaternary Geology. John Wiley & Sons, New York, 1971.

Frakes, Lawrence A.: Climates Throughout Geological Time. Elsevier, London, 1979.

Frazier, K.: The Sun's Back Pages. Mosaic, vol. 12, 1981, pp. 2–8.

Ganapathy, R.: Evidence for a Major Meteorite Impact on the Earth 34 Million Years Ago: Implication for Eocene Extinctions, Science, vol. 216, 1982, pp. 885–886.

Garrels, R.; and Lerman, A.: Phanerozoic Cycles of Sedimentary Carbon and Sulfur. Proc. Nat. Acad. Sci., vol. 78, 1981, pp. 4652–4656.

Garrels, R.; and Perry, E. A.: Cycling of Carbon, Sulfur and Oxygen Through Geologic Time. The sea; Ideas and Observations on Progress in the Study of the Seas, Edward D. Goldberg, ed., vol. 5, Marine Chemistry, Wiley, New York, 1974, pp. 303–336.

Geophysics Study Committee, Geophysics Research Board, Assembly of Mathematical and Physical Sciences, National Research Council: Solar Variability, Weather and Climate. National Academy Press, Washington, D.C., 1982.

Glaessner, Martin F.: Geographic Distribution and Time Range of the Ediacara Precambrian Fauna. Bull. Geol. Soc. Amer., vol. 82, 1971, pp. 509–513.

Glaessner, M. F.: Precambrian. Treatise on Invertebrate Paleontology, Part A, R. A. Robison and C. Teichert, eds., Geol. Soc. Am. and Univ. Kansas Press, Lawrence, Kansas, 1979, pp. A79–A118.

Goldreich, P.: History of the Lunar Orbit. Rev. Geophys., vol. 4, 1966, pp. 411–439.

Goldsmith, D.; and Owen, T.: The Search for Life in the Universe. Benjamin/Cummings Publ. Co., Menlo Park, Calif., 1980.

Grant, V.: Punctuated Equilibria: a Critique. Biol. Zentralblatt, vol. 101, 1982, pp. 175–184.

Gray, Jane; and Boucot, Arthur James: Historical Biogeography, Plate Tectonics and the Changing Environment. Proceedings of the 37th Annual Biology Colloquium, and Selected Papers, Jane Gray and Arthur J. Boucot, eds., Oregon State University Press, Corvallis, Oregon, 1976.

Grieve, R. A. F.; and Dence, M. R.: The Terrestrial Cratering Record. II. The Crater Production Rate. Icarus, vol. 38, 1979, pp. 230-242.

Hallam, A.: Secular Changes in Marine Inundation of USSR and North America Through the Phanerozoic. Nature, vol. 269, 1977, pp. 769-772.

Hamilton, W. D.: The Genetical Evolution of Social Behavior. Jour. Theor. Biol., vol. 7, 1964, pp. 1-32.

Harrington, R. S.: Planetary Orbits in Multiple Star Systems. Life in the Universe, J. Billingham, ed., NASA CP-2156, 1981, pp. 119-123.

Hartmann, William: A "What-If" World Comes to Life in Los Angeles, Smithsonian, vol. 12, no. 12, 1982, pp. 86-94.

Hays, J. D.; Imbrie, John; and Shackleton, N. J.: Variations in the Earth's Orbit: Pacemaker of the Ice Ages. Science, vol. 194, 1976, pp. 1121-1132.

Hays, James D.; and Pitman, Walter C., III: Lithospheric Plate Motion, Sea Level Changes and Climatic and Ecological Consequences. Nature, vol. 246, 1973, pp. 18-22.

Hinegardner, Ralph: Evolution of Genome Size. Molecular Evolution, F. J. Ayala, ed., Sinauer Publ. Co., Sunderland, Mass., 1976, pp. 179-199.

Holland, Heinrich D.: The Chemistry of the Atmosphere and Oceans. Wiley Co., 1978.

Holser, W. T.; and Kaplan, I. R.: Isotope Geochemistry of Sedimentary Sulfates. Chem. Geol., vol. 1, 1966, pp. 93-135.

House, M. R., ed.: The Origin of Major Invertebrate Groups. Academic Press, London, 1979.

Hsü, Kenneth J.: Terrestrial Catastrophe Caused by Cometary Impact at the End of Cretaceous, Nature, vol. 285, 1980, pp. 201–203.

Hsü, K. J.; He, Q.; McKenzie, J. A.; Weissert, H.; Perch-Nielson, K.; Oberhaensli, H.; Kelts, K.; Labreque, J.; Tauxe, L.; and Kraehenbuehl, U.: Mass Mortality and Its Environmental and Evolutionary Consequences. Science, vol. 216, 1982, pp. 249–256.

Imbrie, John; and Imbrie, K. P.: Ice Ages: Solving the Mystery. Enslow Publishers, Short Hills, N.J., 1979.

Imbrie, J.; and Imbrie, J. Z.: Modeling the Climatic Response to Orbital Variations. Science, vol. 207, 1980, pp. 943–953.

Janes, K.: Identifiability of Certain Stars. Life in the Universe, J. Billingham, ed., NASA CP-2156, 1981, pp. 335–342.

Jenkyns, H. C.: Cretaceous Anoxic Events: From Continents to Oceans. Jour. Geol. Soc., London, vol. 137, 1980, pp. 171–188.

Kirschvink, J. L.; Kirk, R.; and Sepkoski, J. J., Jr.: Digital Image Enhancement of Ediacaran Fossils: A First Try (abstract), Geol. Soc. Am. Abst. with Program, vol. 14, 1982, p. 530.

Kollmann, H. A.: Distribution Patterns and Evolution of Gastropods Around the Cretaceous-Tertiary Boundary. Symposium on Cretaceous-Tertiary Boundary Events, Copenhagen, Denmark. II Proceedings Addendum, W. K. Christensen and T. Birkelund, eds., Univ. Copenhagen, Denmark, 1979, pp. 83–87.

Lamb, H. H.: Climate Present, Past, and Future. Methuen, London, vol. 2, 1977.

Lauder, G. V.: Form and Function: Structural Analysis in Evolutionary Morphology. Paleobiology, vol. 7, no. 4, 1981, pp. 340–442.

Lovelock, J. E.: Gaia: a New Look at Life on Earth. Oxford University Press, 1979.

McElhinny, M. W.: Paleomagnetism and Plate Tectonics. Cambridge (Eng.) Univ. Press, 1973.

MacArthur, Robert H.; and Wilson, E. O.: The Theory of Island Biogeography. Princeton Univ. Press, Princeton, N.J., 1967.

Manabe, S.; and Wetherald, R. T.: The Effect of Doubling the CO_2 Concentration on the Climate of a General Circulation Model. Jour. Atmos. Sci., vol. 32, 1975, pp. 3-15.

Margulis, Lynn: Origin of Eukaryotic Cells. Yale Univ. Press, New Haven, Conn., 1970.

Margulis, L.: Symbiosis in Cell Evolution. W. H. Freeman and Co., San Francisco, Calif., 1981.

Marshall, Larry G.; Webb, S. David; Sepkoski, J. John, Jr.; and Raup, David M.: Mammalian Evolution and the Great American Interchange. Science, vol. 215, 1982, pp. 1351-1357.

Martin, P. S.; and Wright, H. E., Jr., eds.: Pleistocene Extinctions: the Search for a Cause. Yale Univ. Press, New Haven, Conn., 1967.

Mayr, Ernst: Animal Species and Evolution. Belknap Press of Harvard Univ. Press, Cambridge, Mass., 1963.

McCrea, W. H.: Ice Ages and the Galaxy. Nature, vol. 255, 1975, pp. 607-609.

McCrea, W. H.: Glaciations and Dense Interstellar Clouds. Nature, vol. 263, 1976, p. 260.

McDonald, G. J. F.: Tidal Friction. Rev. Geophys., vol. 2, 1964, pp. 467-541.

McDonald, G. J. F.: Origin of the Moon: Dynamical Considerations. The Earth-Moon System. B. G. Marsden and A. G. W. Cameron, eds., Plenum Press, New York, 1966, pp. 165-209.

Milankovitch, Milutin: Mathematische Klimalehre und Astronomische Theorie der Klimaschwankungen. Handbuch der Klimatologie I(A), W. Koppen and R. Geiger, eds., Gebr. Borntrager, Berlin, 1930, pp. 1–176.

Milankovitch, M.: Kanon der Erdbestrahlung und sein Andwendung auf das Eiszeitenproblem. Roy. Serb. Acad. Spec. Publ. 132, 1941 (translated by the Israel Program for Scientific Translations, Jerusalem, 1969).

Moore, Raymond C.; Lalicker, C. G.; and Fischer, A. G.: Invertebrate Fossils. McGraw-Hill, New York, 1952.

Munk, Walter H.; and McDonald, G. J. F.: The Rotation of the Earth. Cambridge Univ. Press, New York, 1960.

Neftel, A. H.; Oeschger, H.; Schwander, J.; Stauffer, B.; and Zumbrunn, R.: Ice Core Sample Measurements Give Atmospheric CO_2 Content During the Past 40,000 Years. Nature, vol. 295, 1982, pp. 220–223.

Newell, N. D.: Revolutions in the History of Life. Uniformity and Simplicity, Geol. Soc. Amer. Spec. Paper, vol. 89, Boulder, Colorado, 1967, pp. 63–91.

Newkirk, G., Jr.: Solar Variability on Time Scales of 10^5 to $10^{9.6}$ Years. The Ancient Sun, R. O. Pepin, J. A. Eddy, and R. B. Merrill, eds., Pergamon Press, New York, 1980, pp. 293–320.

Niklas, K. J.; Tiffney, B. H.; and Knoll, A.: Apparent Changes in the Diversity of Fossil Plants. A Preliminary Assessment. Evolutionary Biology, Max Hecht, William Steere, and Bruce Wallace, eds., vol. 12, Plenum Publ. Corp., 1980.

Niklas, K. J.; Tiffney, B. H.; and Knoll, A.: Patterns in Vascular Land Plant Diversity. Nature, vol. 303, 1983, pp. 614–616.

Niklas, K. J.: Simulations of Apical Developmental Sequences in Bryophytes. Ann. Bot., vol. 44, 1979, pp. 339–352.

Niklas, K. J.: Computer Simulations of Early Land Plant Branching Morphologies: Canalization of Patterns During Evolution? Paleobiology, vol. 8, no. 3, 1982, pp. 196–210.

Niklas, K. J.; and O'Rourke, T. D.: Growth Patterns of Plants that Maximize Vertical Growth and Minimize Internal Stresses. Amer. Jour. Botany, vol. 69, no. 9, 1982, pp. 1367–1373.

Opik, E. J.: The Ice Ages. Irish Astron. Jour., vol. 2, 1952, pp. 71–84.

Palmer, A. R.: The Decade of North American Geology 1983 Geologic Time Scale. Geology, vol. 11, 1983, pp. 503–504.

Pitrat, Charles W.: Vertebrates and the Permo-Triassic Extinction. Palaeogeogr., Palaeoclimatol., Palaeoecol., vol. 14, 1973, pp. 249–264.

Pollack, J. B.; Toon, O. B.; Ackerman, T. P.; McKay, C. P.; and Turco, R. P.: Environmental Effects of an Impact-Generated Dust Cloud: Implications for the Cretaceous-Tertiary Extinction. Science, vol. 219, no. 4582, 1983, pp. 287–289.

Rambler, M. B.; and Margulis, L.: Bacterial Resistance to Ultraviolet Radiation Under Anaerobiosis: Implications for Pre-Phanerozoic Evolution. Science, vol. 210, no. 7, 1980, pp. 638–640.

Raup, D. M.: Size of the Permo-Triassic Bottleneck and Its Evolutionary Implications. Science, vol. 260, 1979, pp. 217–218.

Raup, D. M.; and Sepkoski, J. J., Jr.: Mass Extinctions in the Marine Fossil Record. Science, vol. 215, 1982, pp. 1501–1503.

Reid, G. C.: Stratospheric Aeronomy and the Cretaceous-Tertiary Extinctions. Cretaceous-Tertiary Extinctions and Possible Terrestrial and Extraterrestrial Causes, D. A. Russell and P. Beland, eds., Syllogeus 12, Natl. Museums of Canada, 1976, Ottawa, pp. 75–86.

Romer, A. S.: Vertebrate Paleontology. Third ed., Univ. Chicago Press, Chicago, 1966.

Runcorn, S. K.: Paleobiological and Astronomical Observations on the Rotational History of the Earth and Moon. Growth Rhythms and the History of the Earth's Rotation, G. D. Rosenberg and S. K. Runcorn, eds., John Wiley Ltd., London, 1975, pp. 285–291.

Russell, K. L.: Ocean Ridges and Eustatic Changes in Sea Level. Nature, vol. 218, 1968, pp. 861–862.

Russell, D.; and Seguin, R.: Reconstruction of the Small Cretaceous Theropod *Stenonychosaurus inequalis* and a Hypothetical Dinosauroid. Syllogeus 37, Nat. Mus. Nat. Sci., Ottawa, 1982.

Russell, D. A.; and Tucker, W.: Supernovae and the Extinction of the Dinosaurs. Nature, vol. 229, 1971, pp. 553–553.

Salvini-Plawen, L. V.; and Mayr, E.: On the Evolution of Photoreceptors and Eyes. Evolutionary Biology, Max K. Hecht, William C. Steere, and Bruce Wallace, eds., Plenum Press, N.Y., 1977.

Schindewolf, O. H.: Uber die Moglichen Ursachen der Grossen Erdgeschichtlichen Faunenschnitte. Neues Jb. fur Geologie und Palaontologie, Monatschefte, vol. 10, 1954, pp. 457–465.

Schopf, T. J.: Permo-Triassic Extinctions: Relation to Sea Floor Spreading. Jour. Geol., vol. 82, 1974, pp. 129–143.

Schopf, J. W.: Paleobiology of the Precambrian: the Age of Blue-Green Algae. Evol. Biol., vol. 7, 1974, pp. 1–43.

Schneider, Stephen H.; and Dickinson, Robert E.: Climate Modelling. Rev. Geophys. and Space Physics, vol. 12, 1974, pp. 447–493.

Schwarzacher, W.; and Fischer, A. G.: Limestone-Shale Bedding and Perturbations of the Earth's Orbit. Cyclic and Event

Stratification, Gerhard Einsele and Adolf Seilacher, eds.,
Springer-Verlag, Berlin, 1982, pp. 72-93.

Schwarzbach, M.: Climates of the Past. Van Nostrand, Princeton,
N.J., 1963.

Scotese, C. R.: A Continental Drift "Flip Book." Computers and
Geology, vol. 2, 1976, pp. 113-116.

Scotese, C. R.: Continental Drift. Published privately. 5734 S.
Ellis Ave., Chicago, 1979.

Scotese, Christopher R.; Bambach, Richard K.; Barton, Colleen;
Van der Voo, Rob; and Ziegler, Alfred M.: Paleozoic Base
Maps. Jour. Geol., vol. 87, 1979, pp. 217-277.

Sepkoski, J. J., Jr.: A Kinetic Model of Phanerozoic Taxonomic
Diversity: I. Analysis of Marine Orders. Paleobiology, vol. 4,
1978, pp. 223-251.

Sepkoski, J. J., Jr.: A Kinetic Model of Phanerozoic Taxonomic
Diversity: II. Early Phanerozoic Families and Multiple Equilibria. Paleobiology, vol. 5, 1979, pp. 222-251.

Sepkoski, J. J., Jr.: A Factor Analytic Description of the Phanerozoic Marine Fossil Record. Paleobiology, vol. 7, 1981,
pp. 36-53.

Sepkoski, J. J., Jr.: Mass Extinctions in the Phanerozoic Oceans:
A Review. Large Body Impacts and Terrestrial Evolution,
L. T. Silver and P. Schultz, eds., Geol. Soc. Amer. Spec.
Paper 190, 1982.

Shklovskii, I. S.; and Sagan, C.: Intelligent Life in the Universe.
Holden-Day, Inc., San Francisco, Calif., 1966.

Shoemaker, E. M.: Astronomically Observable Crater-Forming
Projectiles. Impact and Explosion Cratering: Planetary and
Terrestrial Implications, D. J. Roddy, R. O. Pepin, and R. B.
Merrill, eds., Pergamon Press, New York, 1977, pp. 617-628.

Shoemaker, E. M.: Collision of Solid Bodies. The New Solar System, J. K. Beatty, B. O'Leary, and A. Chaiken, eds., Sky Publishing Corp., Cambridge University Press, Cambridge, Mass., 1981, pp. 33-44.

Shoemaker, E. M.; Williams, J. G.; Helin, E. F.; and Wolfe, R. F.: Earth-Crossing Asteroids: Orbital Classes, Collision Rates with Earth, and Origin. Asteroids, T. Gehrels, ed., Univ. of Arizona Press, Tucson, 1979, pp. 253-282.

Simberloff, Daniel S.: Permo-Triassic Extinctions: Effects of Area on Biotic Equilibrium. Jour. Geol., vol. 82, 1974, pp. 267-274.

Simpson, George G.: The Major Features of Evolution. Columbia Univ. Press, 1953.

Simpson, G. G.: The History of Life. Evolution after Darwin, the University of Chicago Centennial, vol. I, Sol Tax, ed., Univ. Chicago Press, 1960.

Stanley, S. M.: Macroevolution, Pattern and Process. W. H. Freeman Co., San Francisco, Calif., 1979.

Stanley, S. M.; and Campbell, L. D.: Neogene Mass Extinctions of Western Atlantic Molluscs. Nature, vol. 293, 1981, pp. 257-259.

Stebbins, G. L.: Variation and Evolution in Plants. Columbia Univ. Press, New York, 1950.

Steiner, J.; and Grillmair, E.: Possible Galactic Causes for Periodic and Episodic Glaciations. Bull. Geol. Soc. Am., vol. 84, 1973, pp. 1003-1018.

Stuiver, M.; and Quay, P. D.: Changes in Atmospheric Carbon-14 Attributed to a Variable Sun. Science, vol. 207, 1980, pp. 11-19.

Teichert, C.; McCormick, Lavon; and Williams, Roger B., eds.: Treatise on Invertebrate Paleontology. Second ed., Geol. Soc.

Am., Boulder, Colorado, editions published between 1953 and 1981.

Templeton, A.: Mechanisms of Speciation — a Population Genetic Approach. Ann. Rev. Ecol. Syst., vol. 12, 1981, pp. 23–48.

Terry, K. D.; and Tucker, W. H.: Biologic Effects of Supernovae. Science, vol. 159, 1968, pp. 421–423.

Thierstein, H. R.: Cretaceous Oceanic Catastrophism. Paleobiology, vol. 6, 1980, pp. 244–247.

Thierstein, H. R.: Terminal Cretaceous Plankton Extinctions: a Critical Assessment. Geol. Soc. Amer. Special Paper 190, 1982, pp. 385–399.

Thomson, K. S.: Explanation of Large Scale Extinctions of Lower Vertebrates. Nature, vol. 261, no. 5561, 1976, pp. 578–580.

Tucker, W. H.: Astrophysical Crises in the Evolution of Life in the Galaxy. Life in the Universe, J. Billingham, ed., NASA CP-2156, 1981, pp. 287–296.

Turekian, K. K.: Potential of $^{187}Os/^{186}Os$ as a Cosmic Versus Terrestrial Indicator in High Iridium Layers of Sedimentary Strata. Geol. Soc. Amer. Special Paper 190, 1982, pp. 243–249.

U.S. National Research Council: Research Priorities in Tropical Biology. Nat. Acad. Sciences, Washington, D.C., 1980.

Vail, P. R.; Mitchum, R. M., Jr.; and Thompson, S., III: Seismic Stratigraphy and Global Changes of Sea Level. Part 4. Global Cycles of Relative Changes of Sea Level. Seismic Stratigraphy Applications to Hydrocarbon Exploration, Charles E. Peyton, ed., Amer. Assoc. Petrol. Geol. Memoir 26, Tulsa, Oklahoma, 1977, pp. 83–97.

Valentine, J. W.: Patterns of Taxonomic and Ecological Structure of the Shelf Benthos During Phanerozoic Time. Paleontology, vol. 12, 1969, pp. 684–709.

Valentine, James W.: Evolutionary Paleoecology of the Marine Biosphere. Prentice Hall, Englewood Cliffs, N.J., 1973.

Valentine, J. W.: General Patterns of Metazoan Evolution. Patterns of Evolution as Illustrated by the Fossil Record, Anthony Hallam, ed., Elsevier, Amsterdam, 1977.

Van Valen, L.: Adaptive Zones and the Orders of Mammals. Evolution, vol. 25, 1971, pp. 420-428.

Vanyo, J. P., and Awramik, S. M.: Length of Day and Obliquity of Ecliptic 850 MA Ago: Preliminary Results of a Stromatolite Growth Model. Geophys. Res. Lettrs., vol. 9, no. 10, 1982, pp. 1125-1128.

Veizer, J.; Holser, W. T.; and Wilgus, C. K.: Correlation of $^{13}C/^{12}C$ and $^{34}S/^{32}S$ Secular Variations. Geochm. Cosmochim. Acta, vol. 44, 1980, pp. 579-587.

Walter, M. R.; Oehler, J. H.; and Oehler, D. Z.: Megascopic Algae 1300 Million Years Old from the Belt Supergroup, Montana: A Reinterpretation of Walcott's *Helminthoidichnites*. J. Paleontology, vol. 50, 1976, pp. 872-881.

Watts, A. B.; and Steckler, M. S.: Subsidence and Eustasy at the Continental Margin of Eastern North America. Deep Drilling Results in the Atlantic Ocean: Continental Margins and Paleoenvironment, Maurice Ewing Series, vol. 3, Amer. Geophys. Union, Washington, D.C., 1979, pp. 218-234.

Wells, John W.: Coral Growth and Geochronometry. Nature, vol. 197, no. 4871, 1963, pp. 948-950.

West, R. M.; and Dawson, M. R.: Vertebrate Paleontology and Cenozoic History of the North Atlantic Region. Polarforschung, vol. 48, 1978, pp. 103-119.

Whittaker, R. H.: Evolution of Species Diversity in Land Communities. In: Evolutionary Biology. N. K. Hecht, W. C. Steere, and Bruce V. Wallace (eds.), vol. 10, 1977, pp. 1-68. Plenum Press, N.Y.

Wilson, Edward O.: Insect Societies. Belknap Press of Harvard Univ. Press, Cambridge, Mass., 1971.

Ziegler, A.; Scotese, C.; and Barrett, S.: Mesozoic and Cenozoic Paleogeographic Maps. Tidal Friction and the Earth's Rotation. II. Brosche and Sündermann, eds., Springer-Verlag, Berlin, 1983.

☆ U.S. Government Printing Office. 1985 — 476-669

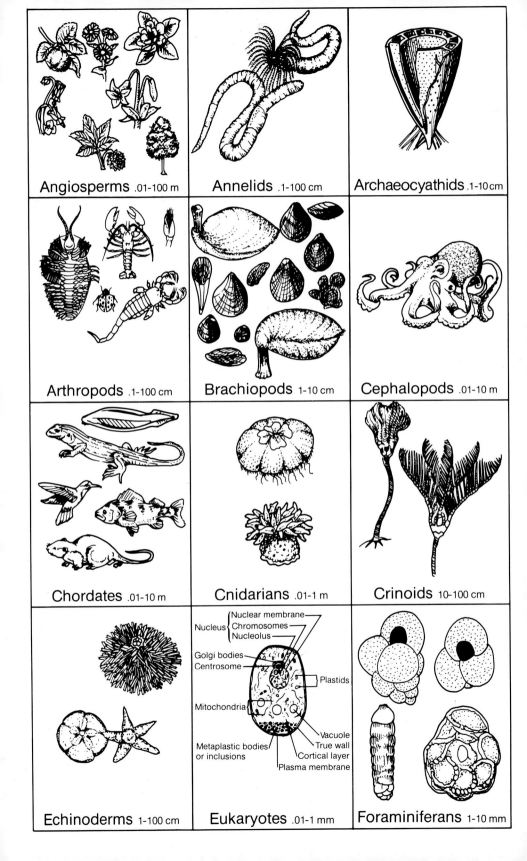

Angiosperms .01-100 m

Annelids .1-100 cm

Archaeocyathids .1-10 cm

Arthropods .1-100 cm

Brachiopods 1-10 cm

Cephalopods .01-10 m

Chordates .01-10 m

Cnidarians .01-1 m

Crinoids 10-100 cm

Echinoderms 1-100 cm

Eukaryotes .01-1 mm

Nuclear membrane
Nucleus { Chromosomes
Nucleolus
Golgi bodies
Centrosome
Plastids
Mitochondria
Vacuole
True wall
Cortical layer
Plasma membrane
Metaplastic bodies
or inclusions

Foraminiferans 1-10 mm